PINACOTECA

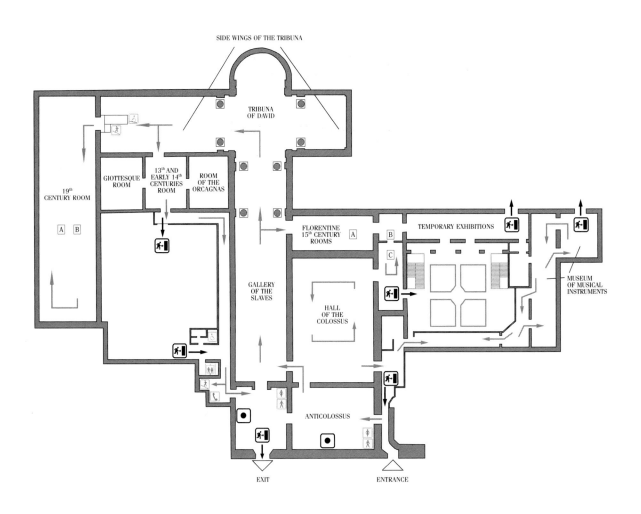

SIDE WINGS OF THE TRIBUNA

TRIBUNA
OF DAVID

19th
CENTURY ROOM

A B

GIOTTESQUE
ROOM

13th AND
EARLY 14th
CENTURIES
ROOM

ROOM
OF THE
ORCAGNAS

FLORENTINE
15th CENTURY
ROOMS

A

B

C

TEMPORARY EXHIBITIONS

MUSEUM
OF MUSICAL
INSTRUMENTS

GALLERY
OF THE
SLAVES

HALL
OF THE
COLOSSUS

ANTICOLOSSUS

EXIT

ENTRANCE

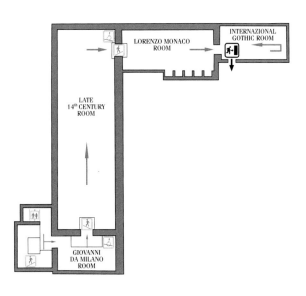

LORENZO MONACO
ROOM

INTERNAZIONAL
GOTHIC ROOM

LATE
14th CENTURY
ROOM

GIOVANNI
DA MILANO
ROOM

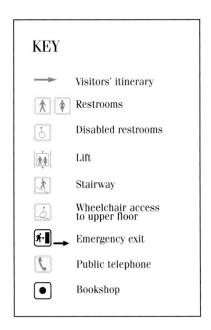

KEY

→ Visitors' itinerary

🚹 🚺 Restrooms

♿ Disabled restrooms

🛗 Lift

🚶 Stairway

♿ Wheelchair access
to upper floor

🏃‍♂️➡️ Emergency exit

📞 Public telephone

⚫ Bookshop

ACCADEMIA GALLERY

The Official Guide
All of the Works

FIRENZE
MVSEI

Texts
Franca Falletti, Marcella Anglani
Gabriele Rossi Rognoni

Revised by
Francesca Ciaravino

Managing Editor
Claudio Pescio

Editor
Augusta Tosone

Translation
Ailsa Wood for Lexis, Florence *and* Catherine Frost

Graphics and page format
Rocío Isabel González *and* Paola Zacchini

Itineraries
Stefano Benini

Photographs
Giunti Archive *and* Foto Rabatti-Domingie, Florence

This guide is a complete catalogue of all the works exhibited in the Gallery, room by room. For each room there is a plan showing the arrangement of the works of art. The encircled numbers refer to the lists in which all the works are catalogued. The small images appearing beside some numbers, in the border around the floor plan, indicate that a comment on these works appears on the following pages.

www. giunti.it

© 1999 Ministero per i Beni e le Attività Culturali –
Soprintendenza Speciale per il Polo Museale Fiorentino

"FIRENZE MVSEI" is a registered trademark
created by Sergio Bianco

First edition: August 1999
Second edition revised: May 2004

Editorial production by Giunti Editore S.p.A., Florence-Milan

Reprint	Year
5 4 3 2 1	2007 2006 2005

Printed by Giunti Industrie Grafiche S.p.A. – Prato (Italy)

Contents

Presentation

ENOUGH BOOKS HAVE *been written about the public museums in Florence run by the Soprintendenza Speciale per il Polo Museale Fiorentino to fill a large library. This is hardly surprising when one considers that the artistic heritage preserved in our museums has been famous throughout the world for centuries. For hundreds of years writers, scholars and travellers of every nationality and country have been attempting to describe all that the Florentine museums contain. They have made great efforts to explain why these museums are so fascinating, and to lead a path through paintings and sculptures for both the uninformed but willing visitor and the refined and jaded intellectual.*

Over time, however, the museums have altered their aspect and their layout, the exhibitions have been arranged in new ways, the collections have been enriched (or impoverished). Attributions of works in the museums have also changed, restorations have transformed the appearance of many pieces, the rise and fall of aesthetic tendencies have led to reorganisation and the exhibition of differing works. All these things are constantly taking place within the public collections because museology and the history of art, like any intellectual endeavour, are in a constant state of progress and transformation. This explains why the literature surrounding the Florentine museums (like that of any of the world's great art collections) is so immense, and in a process of continual updating and change.

The perfect, definitive guide to a museum, any museum, does not and cannot exist.

The premise seems obvious, but is nonetheless necessary in order to understand the point of the publication introduced by these lines. From the moment when, in accordance with the application of the Ronchey Law 4/93, the Giunti publishing house group took over the running of the support services within the Florentine museum system, it was decided to start at once on a standardised series of illustrated guides. These guides, displaying the cuneiform flower of "Firenze Musei" on the cover, guarantee that at the year of publication the state of each museum is exactly that described in the guide.

Certain things are obviously necessary if a museum guide is to aspire to reliability, official standing and at the same time enjoy a wide distribution: accuracy of information, high quality reproductions and – not least – a clearly written text (without, naturally, being banal or lacking in precision). Readers will judge for themselves if the guide which follows this introduction reaches these standards. I have no doubt that this will be a serious and committed judgement, just as myself and the Publisher of this guide have been serious and committed in attempting to meet the cultural needs of whoever visits our museums in the best way and with every possible care.

*The Superintendent
for Polo Museale Fiorentino
Antonio Paolucci*

Introduction

The Accademia Gallery possesses and exhibits an amazing display of almost three hundred paintings covering a span of three centuries (Fourteenth, Fifteenth, and Sixteenth), a unique collection of 88 Russian Icons acquired by the Grand Dukes of Lorraine in the mid-Eighteenth century, and a grandiose Nineteenth century gallery of plaster casts including the original models of the major works of Lorenzo Bartolini and Luigi Pampaloni.

Lastly, in May 2001, a section dedicated to musical instruments was inaugurated, through an agreement stipulated with the nearby 'Luigi Cherubini' State Conservatory of Music, owner of the priceless Collection of instruments that once belonged to the Grand Dukes of Tuscany (the Medici and Lorraine families). The Accademia di Belle Arti from which, as has been seen, this museum originated, had a sector dedicated to musical education, of which the Conservatory is today the heir. With this last acquirement the Galleria has thus re-established links with its historical roots.

A new section now being prepared, that of musical instruments, will open to the public next year, displaying the unique historical collection of the Cherubini Conservatory, linked to the Gallery through special agreements. Obviously, the reasons for visiting this museum are many indeed.

Despite all this, everyone knows that the long, impatient lines of tourists who cross the threshold of the Accademia Gallery each day are really attracted almost exclusively by the myth of Michelangelo's David. *In 1998 there were over a million visitors, many of whom barely glanced at the painting collection and may not even have noticed the Nineteenth century Room. This phenomenon is rather recent, at least in its present frenzied form, and has aroused the curiosity of journalists and authors, historians, psychologists and sociologists. The magic power of the great white fetish is purposely enhanced by the architecture of the hall, which took the shape of a Latin cross when the Gallery of the* Slaves *was built leading up to De Fabris' Tribuna. Moreover, it must be admitted that this hero, already victorious before the fight, represents what modern man is seeking above all else: the reassuring certainty of pure, steadfast strength, a negation of the hesitancy and incertitude of life. And the* Slaves, *with their laborious struggle to emerge from the raw material, seem to have been placed here expressly to arouse an anxiety that the vision of the* David *immediately dispels.*

The heavy sense of the daily struggle to exceed the limitations of human nature is almost overpowering as we enter, but at the back of the great hall lit up by its skylight the world's most famous silhouette already towers above in its stance of classic repose: perfect, calm, in total equilibrium.

Far above any anxious struggle, untouched by defeat, David *exemplifies the secret desire of all.*

*The Director
of the Accademia Gallery
Franca Falletti*

History of the Gallery

a

T he origins of the Accademia Gallery date back to 1784, when the Grand Duke of Tuscany Pietro Leopoldo brought together various art schools and organizations – such as the Accademia delle Arti del Disegno (Academy of Drawing), founded by Giorgio Vasari under the patronage of Cosimo I in 1563 – to form the new Accademia di Belle Arti (Academy of Fine Arts), a public art school.

Two buildings in particular were restructured to create the new Accademia: the Fourteenth century Hospital of San Matteo and the Convent of San Niccolò di Cafaggio. The two great hospital wards for men and for women were rebuilt as well-lit galleries designed to stimulate and instruct young people who had chosen art as a career, while providing them with models to copy. Plaster casts, drawings and models were placed in the former mens'

b

a. Moving Michelangelo's *David*
from Piazza della Signoria
to the Accademia
di Belle Arti Gallery,
from "Nuova Illustrazione
Universale", year I, no. 6,
January 18, 1874, p. 48.

b. Michelangelo's *David*
during transport
to the Accademia di Belle Arti,
Photographic Archives
of the Superintendence
for Artistic and Historical
Patrimony of Florence.

c. Odoardo Borrani,
The Accademia Gallery
in Florence (c. 1860),
oil on canvas, 25x38 cm,
Galleria Nazionale d'Arte
Moderna, Rome.

d. Protection placed around
the *David* during World War II.

e. Constructing protection
around the *David*
during World War II.

f. (p. 13) The Tribuna of *David*
in the Accademia Gallery,
post 1884-ante 1900,
Alinari Brothers photographic
Archives, photo by Brogi.

g. (p. 15) The Tribuna of *David*,
post 1911-ante 1930,
Alinari Brothers photographic
Archives, photo by Brogi.

ward – adjacent to today's *Via Cesare Battisti,*
on the premises of the Accademia di Belle Arti
– while paintings were hung in the former wo-
mens' ward, now the Gallery's Nineteenth century Room.

It was for this educational purpose that the
first core collection of today's Accademia Gallery was formed.

It included, in addition to two grandiose
models by Giambologna – the Rape of the
Sabine women *and* Virtue suppressing Vice –
a number of plaster casts of classical statuary
and a picture gallery consisting of the original collection of the Accademia del Disegno,
which was continuously enriched by paintings transferred here from churches and
monasteries suppressed by Pietro Leopoldo in
1786 and then by Napoleon in 1810.

Pietro Leopoldo also decided that works
awarded prizes in the newly instituted acade-

mic competitions should be kept on perma-
nent display. This gave rise, over the years, to
a gallery presenting a broad sampling of the
activity of teachers and pupils, testifying to
the variety of artistic trends in Tuscany at the
time. The importance of the new acquisitions
is recorded in a description by Carlo Colzi in
1817. The Hall of Great Paintings, also known
as the Galleria di Mezzogiorno (the present
Nineteenth century) contained masterpieces
such as the Santa Trinita Virgin by Cimabue,
the Adoration of the Magi by Gentile da Fabriano, the Baptism of Christ by Verrocchio
and Leonardo, and the Supper at Emmaus by
Pontormo, all of which are now in the Uffizi,
as well as works still in the Accademia Gallery today, including the decorative tiles from
the Santa Croce Reliquary Cabinet by Taddeo
Gaddi, the Annunciation by Lorenzo Monaco
and the Deposition of Christ by Giovanni da

Milano. There were also a number of paintings by Beato Angelico, now in the San Marco Museum.

Not until 1841 was any improvement made in the highly confused arrangement of the paintings, when the President of the Accademia Antonio Ramirez of Montalvo decided to hang them in chronological order to illustrate the history of the Tuscan School from the Fourteenth to the Seventeenth centuries. The remaining Thirteenth and Fourteenth century paintings of unknown attribution or in poor state of conservation were left in the Antique Paintings Gallery (now the Hall of the Slaves) where they were so numerous as to entirely cover the walls. In 1817 there was also a "Prize-winning Works Room" containing eighteen works of art awarded first prize in the triennial painting and sculpture competitions. In 1821 this modern section was enlarged by the addition of prize-winning works from the annual Emulation and Pensionato competitions, all of which remained the property of the Accademia.

When Florence became capital of Italy at the time of the Unification, the city's museums, including the Accademia, underwent great changes. A new addition was the Modern Gallery, consisting of onehundredfortysix works transferred from Palazzo della Crocetta and arranged in six small rooms on the first floor of the Accademia that had previously belonged to the School of Declamation.

The Gallery thus became the first museum of modern art in the new State of Italy. From then on it was mentioned in all of the guidebooks as the Antique and Modern Gallery and increasingly recognized as an attraction for curious travellers as well a place for young artists to study innovations in Florentine art. Numerous requests were made to copy the paintings, the modern ones in particular, clearly demonstrating that the various collections still found a common denominator in the Gallery's educational mission.

In 1872 the museum structure was revolutionized when the Municipal Government decided to build a new room at the end of the Antique Paintings Gallery to house Michelangelo's David, which urgently needed to be moved from its unsheltered outdoor location in Piazza della Signoria. The architect assigned this task, Emilio De Fabris, designed an impressive Tribune which, placed scenographically at the end of the Antique Paintings Gallery and lighted from above by a skylight in the roof, was to welcome the David as the greatest of masterpieces. In early August 1873 the David, sliding on rails through the city streets, was transported to the Accademia where it was left enclosed in a wooden scaffolding for nine years while the Tribuna was being finished.

The arrival of the David and the project for building the Tribuna were crucial events for the fate of the Gallery. In 1875, on the occasion of the fourth centenary of Michelangelo's birth, the Accademia was deemed the most appropriate place to hold an exhibition of copies of the great artist's works. Exhibiting the plaster casts here would have found a valid rationale in the presence of the David, the reference point for the show, in a relationship of mutual enhancement. To create a space large enough for the exhibition it was requested that changes be made in the design of the Tribuna. No longer a square hall, it was to be shaped like a Greek cross. The right wing of the cross would then be extended to connect the Antique Paintings Gallery, then known as the Beato Angelico Gallery, to the parallel one of the Great Paintings, or of Perugino. The Michelangelo exhibition was by far the most important event in the centenary festivities held in Florence on September 13-16, 1875. For the occasion the Tribuna was draped with curtains to conceal the still-unfinished arches and vaults above the trabeation.

The wooden scaffolding was removed and the David, the only original statue in the show, became the fulcrum point of the entire exhibition, towering over all. This event had important museological consequences, giving decisive impetus to the creation of a Michelangelo Museum containing the plaster casts and photographs donated to the City of Florence. With farsighted intuition De Fabris wrote in 1877: "Should the Tribuna be completed, and the Michelangelo Museum inaugurated, it is certain that the proceeds from the sale of tickets would increase substantially, considering that while the importance of the gallery

now is only relative, it would then become so great that no foreigner would come to Florence without visiting it".

The architect Emilio De Fabris was the true artificer of the Michelangelo Museum, inaugurated on July 22, 1882. In the vestibule of the Tribuna, plaster casts of the Medici Tombs were placed against the walls with the seated statues of Lorenzo and Giuliano de' Medici above them. At the back of the Tribuna's left wing, the shorter one, stood the Moses. In the right wing were plaster casts of the artist's most famous works; at the center, under the tribunal arch, was a copy of the St. Peter's Pietà, while copies of the Rondanini Pietà and the Minerva Christ were placed at the corners of the piers.

In that same 1882 management of the Accademia's Antique and Modern Gallery was transferred from the Fine Arts Institute to the Museums Bureau, causing the conservational, historical and documentary functions of the museum to prevail over the promotional program for contemporary art. In fact, as long as academic teaching methods had been based on the exercise of copying, the picture gallery had remained closely bound to the Accademia's painting School. When that method was abandoned as obsolete and inconsonant with the needs of contemporary art, the emancipation of the galleries from academic control became an urgent necessity.

The separation of the Antique and Modern Gallery from the art school was underlined by the opening of a new entrance in Via Ricasoli and by re-arrangement of the Michelangelo Museum.

The position of the Tribuna remained the same up to the early Twentieth century, while the Antique Paintings sector underwent major changes that marked the end of a trend of scientific and vaguely positivistic museum culture. Moreover, the concept of the museum as a structure dedicated exclusively to conservation was undergoing revision at this time, in relation to a new way of confronting works of art, now considered to be the subject of pure contemplation and "not a series of objects to be arranged in rows like insects by entomologists, but living things".

These new museum concepts was to influence the program for rearranging the Florentine galleries carried out by Cosimo Ridolfi, the Director from 1890 to 1903. During this period the Accademia Gallery definitively lost its original characteristics, as profound changes were made. In the first place, the works of art in the Great Paintings Gallery urgently needed restoration, and this was favorable to a new arrangement. Wooden partitions were used to divide the room into three areas, separating the Fourteenth and Fifteenth century paintings from those of the Seventeenth century.

Three new rooms were also created (the former Byzantine Rooms the actually Thirteenth and Early Fourteenth centuries Room, Room of the Orcagnas and their followers, Giottesque Room) along the left wing of the Tribuna, providing a more dignified and luminous setting for the paintings of Botticelli (to whom two of the rooms were dedicated), of Perugino and their pupils. Ridolfi made these changes to adapt the Accademia Gallery to the new aesthetic appreciation of the Florentine Fifteenth Century School then being proclaimed mainly by British collectors living in Florence.

The rediscovery of Botticelli, which had begun with Pater's studies and been confirmed by the extensive monograph written by Herbert Horne during his years in Florence, was becoming a real cult in the early years of the Twentieth century, generating great public enthusiasm. A period of renewed popularity suddenly opened up for the Accademia Gallery, with its numerous Fifteenth century paintings. With the dignity and prominence conferred on them by their new arrangement, these paintings became a pole of attraction equal to or greater than that of the David and Michelangelo's other works.

Ridolfi then decided to put in "more appropriate state" the hall leading to the Tribuna, where Thirteenth and Fourteenth century panels and polyptychs were amassed in utter confusion. Radical changes were made in the arrangement of this hall. The paintings were removed and the walls adorned with rich tapestries depicting Stories of Adam and Eve. Plaster casts of some of Michelangelo's minor works were placed along both side walls. The

paintings that had been removed were then hung in the three rooms adjoining the Hall (now the Florentine Rooms), suitably decorated and lighted, the first of which was dedicated to Beato Angelico. This arrangement lasted only a few years since in 1919 works of capital importance to the Florentine School – Giotto and Cimabue's Majesty, Gentile da Fabriano's Adoration of the Magi, Masolino and Masaccio's Saint Anne Metterza, Botticelli's Primavera and many others were moved to the Uffizi Gallery, and in 1922 the conspicuous group of paintings by Beato Angelico went to establish the new San Marco Museum. Almost contemporaneously, in 1914, an agreement was stipulated between the State and the Municipality to group various collections of modern art in a single museum set up in 1920 on the second floor of Palazzo Pitti. The modern works of the Accademia Gallery, in part dispersed among various State and Municipal storage deposits, were transferred to their new home.

After having lost so many of its paintings the Gallery could no longer call itself the Antique and Modern Gallery. From now on it was to be Accademia Gallery or, for a few more years, Michelangelo Museum. The arrangement of the latter has also undergone numerous changes up to the present.

Controversy over the arrangement of the museum flared up again in the first decade of the Twentieth century, in relation to the question of placing a copy of the David in Piazza della Signoria. The presence of plaster casts in a public gallery, inserted within a context still linked to educational ideals and positivist/historical objectives, now seemed entirely unjustified. In line with the new aesthetic canons, authenticity became the guiding principle of the Gallery's Director Corrado Ricci, and most of the plaster casts kept here since the centenary exhibition were removed and replaced by original works of Michelangelo. At the same time, national newspapers were calling attention to the poor state of the Slaves in Buontalenti's Grotto in the Boboli Gardens, and to the St. Matthew "drowsing under the atrium of the Accademia". The Slaves were removed from Boboli, replaced by copies, and transferred to the Accademia Gallery in 1909.

That same year the School of Accademia delle Belle Arti, which had already contributed the model of the Fiume Torso in 1906, donated the St. Matthew. This group of works was further enriched by the Victory, transferred from the Bargello Museum in 1905. The plaster casts from the centenary exhibition, arranged by Ridolfi along the walls hung with tapestries, were replaced by the originals of the Slaves, the St. Matthew and the Victory, along with two plaster casts of the Louvre Slaves, while the model of the Fiume Torso was placed under the right arch of the Tribuna. The plaster casts of the Tombs, the Moses, the Rondanini Pietà, the Minerva Christ and the Vatican Pietà remained in their original places. In Ricci's arrangement based on the principle of authenticity, even these last plaster casts soon appeared inappropriate. However, it was only in 1938 that the casts of the two Pietà, the Moses, the Minerva Christ and the Tombs were definitively moved to the Plaster Casts Collection of the Porta Romana Art School. The two casts of the Slaves were the last to leave the Accademia in 1946, transferred first to the Casa Buonarroti Museum, then to the House of Michelangelo in Caprese, where a conspicuous group of casts from the centennial exhibition can still be seen today.

The collection of the originals also underwent changes before taking on its present-day aspect. In 1921, with the closure of the Dante Year and the celebration of victory in World War I, Ugo Ojetti suggested that, for the occasion, the Victory should be brought back to the Hall of the Five Hundred in Palazzo Vecchio. In 1939 the State of Italy purchased for the Accademia the Palestrina Pietà, coming from a chapel in Palazzo Barberini at Palestrina, the authenticity of which is now denied by the most authoritative scholars. Lastly, in 1965, the Fiume Torso was requested by Charles Tolnay, to join the other models in the Casa Buonarroti.

In the 1930s the Hall of the Colossus and that of the Anticolossus were annexed to the Gallery. These large rooms provided a perfect setting for the great altarpieces of the Florentine Sixteenth century masters such as Massimo Albertinelli, Bronzino, Alessandro Allori, Santi di Tito, and Passignano.

After the war, during rearrangement of the Uffizi Gallery, some large paintings were moved to the Accademia, including the Sixteenth century Assumption by Perugino and Deposition by Perugino and Filippino Lippi.

In the 1950s, under the direction of Luisa Becherucci, the Hall of the Colossus, illustrating the course of art in the Fifteenth and Sixteenth centuries, was organized on a more historical basis, as can be seen in the works of Perugino, Fra Bartolomeo, Granacci, Bugiardini and Sogliani. In the Hall of the Anticolossus, now occupied by the bookshop and ticket office, were placed some works coming from the Uffizi, including the Young St. John from the school of Raphael and the Venus and Cupid by Pontormo. These works, in addition to those of Bronzino and Allori already present, clearly illustrated the development of the "modern manner" in the Sixteenth century. Only in the 1980s was this arrangement dismantled and the paintings hung in the Tribuna in place of the tapestries, to underline their direct and indirect relationship with the work of Michelangelo.

Subsequent Directors have opposed the tendency – which had emerged in the post-World War I period – to proceed without a specific direction or long-term project. From direction of Luciano Bellosi, through the important years of Giorgio Bonsanti, up to the current Director Franca Falletti, a continuous attempt has been made to trace a guiding principle on which to construct the identity of the Accademia Gallery.

This project took concrete shape in the years between 1983 and 1985 with the arrangement of the Nineteenth century Room and that of the Late Fourteenth century Room on the first floor, supervised by Angelo Tartuferi in 1998. The opening to the public of the latter rooms confirmed the museum's chronological, stylistic and historical direction, providing a continuous panorama, albeit in different groups of rooms, of Florentine art from the late Thirteenth to the late Sixteenth centuries, in accordance with the original principles of the Accademia as conceived by Pietro Leopoldo. What now re-emerges in all its significance is the value of the Accademia as school of instruction and exemplification of the highest artistic manifestations in three centuries of history. Within this context, the Collection of Russian Icons on the first floor also testifies to the precious heritage of the Lorraine family.

The Nineteenth century Room, with the plaster casts by Bartolini and Pampaloni and the paintings, few but significant, by pupils and professors of the Accademia di Belle Arti, unites the Accademia to the Gallery, rebuilding a bridge of historical significance and recalling how Accademia and Gallery were once joined in a common project to produce and nourish art.

As the origins of the Gallery have been retrieved, links with the adjoining Cherubini Conservatory and Opificio delle Pietre Dure have inevitably been restored. All of these institutions, in fact, grew out of a unified project, perhaps the most culturally significant initiative of the Lorraine government, that of constructing, in the block between today's Via Ricasoli, Via degli Alfani, Via dei Servi and Via Cesare Battisti, a true citadel of the arts. This is the basis for the current Director's project, in which a Museum of Musical Instruments, containing the historic collection of the Cherubini Conservatory, has been opened to the public. And it is possible that in the near future the itinerary may be completed by coordinated access to the Museum of the Opificio delle Pietre Dure, next door to the Cherubini Conservatory.

The Museum of Musical Instruments

MUSIC AT THE MEDICEAN COURT

The Museum of Musical Instruments in the Accademia Gallery, inaugurated in 2001, currently exhibits over forty instruments from the 17th, 18th and 19th centuries, coming from the Grand-Ducal collections of the Medici and Lorraine families. The collection is owned by the 'Luigi Cherubini' Conservatory of Florence, which received the instruments and carefully preserved them since the 19th century. The exhibition includes some objects unique the world over, such as the Tenor Viola *by Antonio Stradivari, the only instrument created by the famous violin-maker which has been entirely kept in its original state; the earliest known example of an* Upright Piano; *and an* Oval Spinet, *the first instrument constructed for the Medici family by the inventor of the piano, Bartolomeo Cristofori. The cultural and musical context for which these instruments were created is illustrated by some seventeenth-century paintings portraying musicians and their instruments at the Medicean Court. In addition, a computerized multimedia system provides visitors with information in Italian and English on the history and particular features of these instruments, and even allows them to hear their sound. In addition, some models which can be actuated by visitors illustrate the action of the first Piano, invented at the Medicean Court in the late 17th century, and show how this instrument differs from its forerunner, the* Harpsichord.

The instruments

1. NICOLÒ AMATI
Violoncello
Cremona, c. 1650
Spruce and maple wood
Inv. Cherubini 1988/33

2. FABRIZIO SENTA
Violoncello
Turin, 1667
Spruce and maple wood
Inv. Cherubini 1988/37

3. ROCCO DONI
Violoncello
1696
Cypress and maple wood
Inv. Cherubini 1988/40

4. MICHELE ANTONIO GRANDI (ATTR.)
Marble Dulcimer
Carrara (?), post 1691
Statuary marble, bardiglio,
and broccatello giallo
Inv. Cherubini 1988/88

5. ANTONIO STRADIVARI
'Medici' Tenor Viola
Cremona, 1690
Spruce and maple wood
Inv. Cherubini 1988/15

6. ANTONIO STRADIVARI
'Medici' Violoncello
Cremona, 1690
Spruce and maple wood
Inv. Cherubini 1988/34

7. ANONYMOUS
Double Bass
Italy, mid-18th century
Spruce and maple wood
Inv. Cherubini 1988/45

8. BARTOLOMEO CRISTOFORI (?)
Double Bass
Florence, 1715
Spruce and maple wood
Inv. Cherubini 1988/41

9. ANTONIO STRADIVARI
"Medici" Violin
Cremona, 1716
Spruce and maple wood
Inv. Cherubini 1988/3

10. ANTONIO CASINI (ATTR.)
Violin
Modena, second half 17th century
Spruce and maple wood
Inv. Cherubini 1988/2

11. ANONYMOUS
Violin
Northern Italian School, mid-18th century
Spruce and maple wood
Inv. Cherubini 1988/1

12. BARTOLOMEO CRISTOFORI
Ebony Harpsichord
Florence, ante 1700
Ebony and cypress, ivory
Inv. Cherubini 1988/101

13. BARTOLOMEO CRISTOFORI
Oval spinet
Florence, 1690
Rosewood and cypress, ivory
Inv. Eredità Bardini no. 3376

14. BARTOLOMEO CRISTOFORI (ATTR.)?
Pianoforte action
Florence, post 1722
Chestnut and boxwood, cardboard, leather
Kraus Collection Inv. no. 1

15. DOMENICO DEL MELA
Upright piano
Galliano nel Mugello (Florence), 1739
Coniferous wood, cypress and boxwood
Inv. Cherubini 1988/110

16a. JOHANN CASPAR JOSEPH EINBIGLER (ATTR.)
Pair of kettle-drums
(?), c. 1837
Copper, iron, leather
Inv. Cherubini 1988/199, 209

16b. ANONYMOUS
Pair of jingles
(?), late 18th century
Iron and bronze
Inv. Cherubini 1988/204, 212

16c. ANONYMOUS
Pair of castanets
(?), mid-19th century
Boxwood
Inv. Cherubini 1988/203, 211

16d. ANONYMOUS
Pair of triangles
(?), mid-18th century
Iron
Inv. Cherubini 1988/201, 206

16e. ANONYMOUS
Pair of xylophones
(?), mid-18th century
Rosewood
Inv. Cherubini 1988/202, 210

17a. JOSEPH HUSCHAUER
Trio of trombones
Vienna, 1813
Brass
Inv. Cherubini 1988/182-184

17b. MICHAEL SAURLE
Pair of natural horns with crooks
Munich, 1807
Brass
Inv. Cherubini 1988/192-193

17c. ANONYMOUS
Post-horn
Austria (?), ante 1819
Brass
Inv. Cherubini 1988/191

18a. FRIEDRICH GABRIEL AUGUST KIRST
Piccolo with corps de rechange
Potsdam, ante 1806
Boxwood and horn
Inv. Cherubini 1988/118

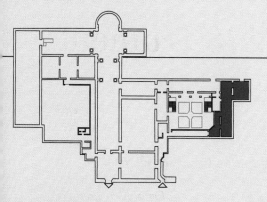

18b.VINATIERI AND CASTLAS
Piccolo in G
Turin, c. 1838
Boxwood and horn
Inv. Cherubini 1988/117

18c.VINATIERI AND CASTLAS
Clarinet in G
Turin, c. 1838
Boxwood and horn
Inv. Cherubini 1988/159

18d.VINATIERI AND CASTLAS
*Five clarinets in E-flat
with corps de rechange in D*
Turin, c. 1838
Boxwood and horn
Inv. Cherubini 1988/160-164

18e.WOLFGANG KÜSS (KIES)
*Basset-horn in F
with corps de rechange*
Vienna, 1810-1819
Maplewood and brass
Inv. Cherubini 1988/167

18f. LORENZO CERINO
Serpent
Turin, late 18th century
Chestnut wood (?) and leather
Inv. Cherubini 1988/175

19. ANONYMOUS
Trumpet Marine
(?), c. 1790
Silver fir, cherry and walnut
Inv. Cherubini 1988/47

20. JEAN NICOLAS LAMBERT
Pair of hurdy-gurdies
Paris, 1775
Mahogany, maple, beech,
ebony, ivory
Inv. Cherubini 1988/50-51

21. NIKOLAUS DOPFER
Viola
Magonza, 1774
Spruce and maple wood
Inv. Cherubini 1988/19

22. DODDS & CLAUS
Piano-guitar
New York, c. 1793
Coniferous and maple wood
Inv. Cherubini 1988/76

23. ANONYMOUS
Guitar with six strings
(?), ante 1804
Spruce and exotic wood
Inv. Cherubini 1988/73

The paintings

24. ANTON DOMENICO GABBIANI
*The Grand Prince Ferdinando
with his musicians*
1685 (?)
Oil on canvas; 139×221
Inv. 1890 no. 2808 (on loan
from the Palatina Gallery, Florence)

25. ANTON DOMENICO GABBIANI
Musicians of the Grand Prince
1685 (?)
Oil on canvas; 140×233
Inv. 1890 no. 2805 (on loan
from the Palatina Gallery, Florence)

26. IMITATOR OF BASCHENIS
*Still life with drapes, box,
book, fruit, globe, guitar,
violin, violoncello with bow,
lute, mandola, recorder*
last quarter of the 17th century
Oil on canvas; 105×148
Inv. 1890 no. 5781 (on loan
from the Palatina Gallery, Florence)

27. BARTOLOMEO BIMBI
*Still life with lute,
viola with bow,
sheet with musical score,
cabinet, small boxes,
orange, clarion, trumpet,
violin, flute, books,
armillary sphere, guitar,
Turkish carpet, drapes*
Ante 1702
Oil on canvas; 51×66
Inv. 1890 no. 5801
(on loan from the
Palatina Gallery, Florence)

28. ANTON DOMENICO GABBIANI
Portrait of musician with lute
c. 1685-1690
Oil on canvas; 130×95
Inv. Poggio Imperiale 1860 no. 67
(on loan from the Educandato
della SS. Annunziata at Poggio
Imperiale, Florence).
Restored: 2001.

29. ANTON DOMENICO GABBIANI
*Trio of musicians
of the Grand Prince Ferdinando
with a Moorish servant*
1687 (?)
Oil on canvas; 141×208
Inv. 1890 no. 2802 (on loan
from the Palatina Gallery, Florence)

30.CRISTOFORO MUNARI
*Still life with bucchero, lute, cups,
carpet, fruit, violoncello with bow,
recorder, sheets with musical score*
c. 1707-1713
Oil on canvas; 175×147
Inv. 1890 no. 5139 (on loan
from the Palatina Gallery, Florence)

31. CRISTOFORO MUNARI
*Musical panoply with cornet,
recorder, violin with bow, mandolin*
c. 1707-1713
Oil on canvas; 65×49
Inv. 1890 no. 7745 (on loan
from the Palatina Gallery, Florence)

32. ANTON DOMENICO GABBIANI
*Trio of musicians
of the Grand Prince Ferdinando*
1687 (?)
Oil on canvas; 114×153
Inv. 1890 no. 2807 (on loan
from the Palatina Gallery, Florence)

1 **3**

THE MEDICEAN VIOLONCELLOS

The three Cellos are listed in an Inventory of the instruments belonging to the personal collection of Grand Prince Ferdinando de' Medici, compiled in the year 1700. The one bearing the Medici coat-of-arms was built by the violin-maker from Cremona Nicolò Amati, active between 1630 and 1670, and probably the master of Antonio Stradivari. The body of the instrument, originally larger, was 'trimmed' in the late 18th century to reduce its size to the dimensions that had become standard for cellos after the beginning of 1700.

NICOLÒ AMATI
Violoncello

Cremona, c. 1650
Red spruce and maple wood

Total length 122 cm
Body measurements:
length 75,7 cm;
maximum width 45,7 cm
Inv. Cherubini 1988/33

4

MARBLE DULCIMER

The *Dulcimer* is an instrument that was extraordinarily popular in Italy in the 17th and 18th centuries, only to disappear completely in the Romantic age. With the ingenious arrangement of the strings, which were plucked with plectra fastened to the fingertips, a wide range of notes can be played with this small instrument. The one exhibited here is truly unique in that it is entirely constructed of marble of three different kinds (white statuary marble, bardiglio from Carrara and yellow broccatello) rather than wood. The dedication and the painting on the cover of the case show that it was built for Grand Duke Cosimo III de' Medici, the father of Grand Prince Ferdinando, after 1691. It was probably the work of the same artisan who built for the Este family a *Guitar*, a *Violin*, a *Harpsichord* and various wind instruments, all in the same material. Although these instruments were designed primarily as decorative objects, they could perfectly well be played.

MICHELE ANTONIO GRANDI
(ATTR.)
Marble Dulcimer
Carrare (?), After 1691

Statuary marble, bardiglio,
and yellow broccatello
Maximum width 74,5 cm;
depth 30 cm
Inv. Cherubini 1988/88

THE MEDICEAN QUINTET

The *Tenor Viola* and the *Violoncello* formed part of a 'quintet' of string instruments (two *Violins*, an *Alto Viola*, a *Tenor Viola* and a *Violoncello*) built by the master from Cremona Antonio Stradivari for Grand Prince Ferdinando and dated 1690. The five instruments were all decorated with the Medici coat-of-arms in mother-of-pearl, and with ebony and ivory inlays. The chosen woods, of exceptional quality, combined excellent sound with the highest aesthetic value. The *Tenor Viola* is the only instrument in the world made by Antonio Stradivari to be entirely conserved in its original state; as such, it represents a document of inestimable importance for violin-makers and music scholars. The large size of the *Viola* body, like that of the *Violoncello*, intensifies the bass sounds and confers on the instruments a characteristic deep timbre.

ANTONIO STRADIVARI
'Medici' Tenor Viola
Cremona, 1690
Red spruce and maple wood
Total length 75,5 cm

Body measurements:
length 47,8 cm;
maximum width 27,1 cm
Inv. Cherubini 1988/15

VIOLINS

The three *Violins* were acquired for the Grand-Ducal Collection at a relatively late time (after 1814), but were constructed during the lifetime of Grand Prince Ferdinando. The red-varnished *Violin* is one of the best conserved instruments built by Antonio Stradivari. It dates from the period of full stylistic maturity of the Master, who established the classic proportions and lines for the violin makers in Cremona, still today taken as model by violin-makers all over the world. The other two instruments, of the Modena and the Po Valley schools, differ from each other in the color of the varnish, the contour of the belly, the shape of the f-holes and the form of the scroll. On the basis of this and other stylistic features, their authorship (falsely indicated on labels glued to the inside of the body) has been questioned and the current attribution has been proposed.

ANTONIO STRADIVARI
'Medici' Violin

Cremona, 1716
Red spruce
and maple wood
Total length 59,7 cm
Body measurements:
length 35,8 cm;
maximum width 20,8 cm
Inv. Cherubini 1988/3

12–15

KEYBOARD INSTRUMENTS

The *Piano*, a keyboard instrument whose strings are struck by hammers, was invented in Florence shortly before 1700 by a Paduan instrument-maker, Bartolomeo Cristofori, at the service of Grand Prince Ferdinando, and was only the most long-lasting of his numerous and ingenious inventions. Exhibited in the same room is the first instrument created by him for the Medici: a *Spinet* recently rediscovered, whose form, action and sonority were entirely designed by Cristofori. Dating from slightly later, also built for the Medici, is a *Harpsichord* constructed entirely of ebony wood. The action displayed at the left of the *Spinet* seems instead to come from a pianoforte dating from Cristofori's time, although its attribution to a specific maker is still debatable. The instrument displayed on the opposite side of the hall is the earliest known *Upright Piano*. It was built in 1739, seven years after the death of Cristofori, by an instrument-maker who may have been his assistant, Domenico del Mela.

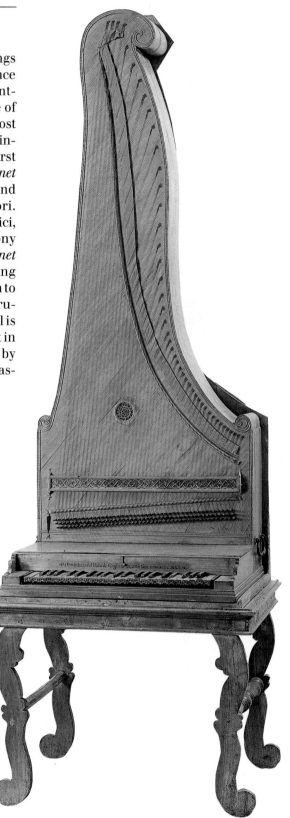

DOMENICO DEL MELA
Upright Piano

Galliano nel Mugello (Florence),
1739

Coniferous wood,
cypress and boxwood
Total height 273 cm;
width 93 cm; depth 64 cm
Compass: Do1/Mi1-Do5 (C/E-c''')
Inv. Cherubini 1988/110,

MUSIC IN THE LORRAINE AGE

When the sovereignty of the Grand-Duchy of Tuscany passed from the Medici family (which died out in 1737) to the Austrian one of the Lorraines, radical changes occurred in the musical life of the Court and that of the entire city. Grand Duke Pietro Leopoldo (ruler of Florence from 1765) promoted public musical events, held in the streets and squares, as well as celebrations open on occasion to the citizens as a whole. This new approach was reflected in the collection of musical instruments as well. Many of the instruments from Medicean times, worn and unsuited to the new activity of the Court, were sold or discarded, and new ones – wind and percussion instruments in particular – were purchased and imported from abroad.

PERCUSSION INSTRUMENTS

The percussion instruments exhibited here represent one of the very rare homogenous groups of this kind which has survived from the late 18th century. These instruments were used for the most part in theatrical performances and Court balls. Among them is the oldest pair of *Kettle-drums* in Italy, equipped with a tuning mechanism, in addition to pairs of *Jingles* used "for the waltz of the whip", *Xylophones*, *Castanets* and *Triangles*.

JOHANN CASPAR JOSEPH EINBIGLER (?)
Pair of kettle-drums
c. 1837

Copper, iron, leather
Height of the drumhead
from the ground 80 cm;
diameter of the drumheads:
50/53 cm
Inv. Cherubini 1988/199, 209

WIND INSTRUMENTS

After the Restoration of the Lorraines in 1814, subsequent to fifteen years of French domination, various wind instruments were purchased for both theatrical use and performances of the Grand-Ducal band. The brass instruments, *Horns* and *Trombones*, were imported from Germany and Austria and may have been brought to Florence by members of the Court. The provenance of the little *Post-horn* (before 1819) is instead unknown, but the instrument is of a type that had been commonly used since the early 16th century by couriers in the postal service to announce their arrival at a post station. In the nineteenth century the little instrument was used to limited extent for special effects in the orchestra. The next display case holds wind instruments made of wood. Some of them, a *Piccolo* (before 1806), a *Basset-Horn* (1810-1819) and the five *Clarinets* (from about 1838) are furnished with *corps de rechange* which could be substituted to the original ones to change the intonation and make it more acute. Some others, such as the *Serpent* and the above-mentioned *Basset-Horn*, are constructed so that the size of these quite long instruments can be reduced, making them more manageable. The *Serpent* was widely used as bass accompaniment for religious and military music, while passages for the *Basset-Horn* were composed by W. A. Mozart, among others.

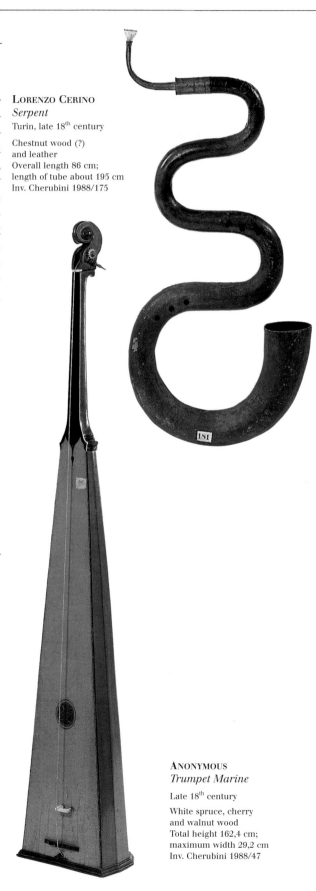

LORENZO CERINO
Serpent
Turin, late 18th century

Chestnut wood (?)
and leather
Overall length 86 cm;
length of tube about 195 cm
Inv. Cherubini 1988/175

THE TRUMPET MARINE

The sound of this instrument with a single catgut string is extraordinarily similar to that of a trumpet, thanks to an asymmetrical bridge that rests on only one of its two feet, while the other rattles on the soundboard when the string is bowed. This instrument, which entered the Grand-Ducal Collection in the late 18th century, was used in musical performances held at the Lorraine Court until the 1830s.

It was specifically required in the score of an opera presented at Court, the *Socrate immaginario* by Giovanni Paisiello, in which an instrumental solo is followed by an aria ("Questa corda non s'accorda al dio Amor" [this string is not in tune with the god of Love]), a humorous allusion to the instrument's harsh timbre.

ANONYMOUS
Trumpet Marine

Late 18th century

White spruce, cherry
and walnut wood
Total height 162,4 cm;
maximum width 29,2 cm
Inv. Cherubini 1988/47

HURDY-GURDIES

The sound of the *Hurdy-gurdy* is produced by a number of strings set in vibration by a wooden wheel coated with rosin, driven by a crank, which strokes the strings like the bow of a violin. The notes are produced by pressing a series of keys on the side with the left hand. Instruments based on this principle had been known in Europe since the 13th century, but only in the 18th this model, richly decorated with mother-of-pearl and inlays, was developed specifically for amateur musicians among the nobility. The *Hurdy-gurdy* became especially popular in France, since the wife of Louis XV was in fact an accomplished player on this instrument. In a parallel development, a 'popular' model, much cruder in appearance but functioning in the same way and used mainly by beggars, survived throughout the 19th century.

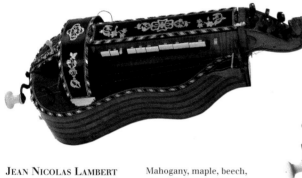

JEAN NICOLAS LAMBERT
Pair of Hurdy-gurdies

Paris, 1775

Mahogany, maple, beech, ebony, ivory
Body measurements:
length 46,1 cm;
maximum width 24,5 cm
Inv. Cherubini 1988/50-51

THE VIOLA AND THE GUITARS

The *Viola*, the *Piano-Guitar* and the *Guitar with six strings* entered the Lorraine Collection in the early 19th century. The *Viola* (1774) presents the typical characteristics of a German-made instrument: dark varnish, short, vertical f-holes, pronounced arching of the belly and back. The *Piano-Guitar* is, instead, an instrument constructed in the United States near the end of the 18th century, but designed in Great Britain as a particular version of the *English Guitar*, with drop-shape case, flat belly and back. It was an instrument designed for well-brought up young girls, in which the strings are struck by a series of hammers actioned by six keys, ensuring that the player's fingertips are not roughened. The *Guitar with six strings*, despite some modifications made to the original structure, has kept the slender proportions of the body typical of instruments built in the first half of the 19th century. This instrument was played, it seems, by Queen Maria Luisa di Borbone-Parma (1807).

ANONYMOUS
Guitar with six strings

ante 1804
Spruce and exotic wood
Total length 91,5 cm
Body measurements:
length 43,2 cm
maximum width 26,1 cm
Inv. Cherubini 1988/73

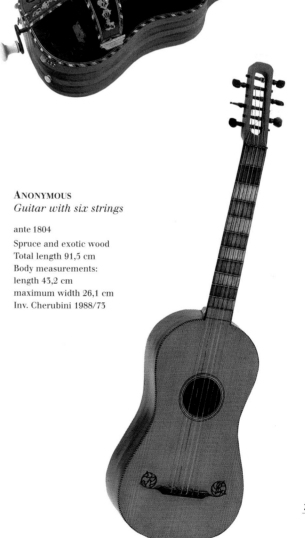

Hall of the Colossus

The name of this room is not, as is usually believed, taken from Giambologna's plaster model, now placed at its centre, but from the model of one of Montecavallo's Dioscuri, displayed here in the last century. The panels on display follow on in chronological order from the route of the Florentine rooms and are therefore by painters working in the early decades of the Sixteenth century.

The works

1. RIDOLFO DEL GHIRLANDAIO
(above)
Six Angels in Prayer
c. 1510
Oil on wood
111×54 cm (each)
Inv. 1890 nos. 8648 and 8649

2. FRANCESCO GRANACCI (below)
Stories of Saints
(*Martyrdom of St Apollonia,
Disputation of St Catherine,
Martyrdom of St Catherine,
A Saint before the Judge, Martyrdom
of a Saint, Martyrdom of a Saint*)
c. 1530
Oil on wood (two panels)
48×194 (upper panel)
51×212 (lower panel)
Inv. 1890 nos. 8690, 8691, 8692,
8693-8694, 8695

3. FRANCESCO GRANACCI
Madonna with Child and Saints
c. 1510
Oil on wood
210×192 cm
Inv. 1890 no. 3247
Restored: 1994

4. FRANCESCO GRANACCI
Virgin of the Girdle
1500-1520
Oil on wood
312×194 cm
Inv. 1890 no. 1596

5. FRANCESCO GRANACCI
*Assumption of the Virgin
and Saints*
c. 1510
Oil on wood
231×252 cm
Inv. 1890 no. 8650

6. MARIOTTO ALBERTINELLI
The Holy Trinity
c. 1510
Oil on wood
237,5×137,5 cm
Inv. 1890 no. 8660

7. RIDOLFO DEL GHIRLANDAIO
*Madonna with Child
and Saints*
1503
Oil on wood
184×167 cm
Inv. 1890 no. 4652

8. PÉRUGIN
Assumption of the Virgin
1500
Oil on wood
435×266 cm
Inv. 1890 no. 8366

**9. FILIPPINO LIPPI
AND PIETRO PERUGINO**
Deposition
1504 and 1507
Oil on wood; 356×247 cm
Inv. 1890 no. 8370
Restored: 1997

10. GIOVANNI ANTONIO SOGLIANI
*Dispute concerning
the Immaculate Conception*
c. 1530
Oil on wood
374,5×260 cm
Inv. 1890 no. 3203

11. ANDREA DEL SARTO
Christ as the Man of Sorrows
c. 1525
Detached fresco
200×131,5 cm
Inv. 1890 no. 8675

12. RIDOLFO DEL GHIRLANDAIO
*Removal of the body
of St. Zanobius*
c. 1516
Oil on wood
220×191 cm
Inv. 1890 no. 1589

13. MARIOTTO ALBERTINELLI
Annunciation
1510
Oil on wood
345×247 cm
Inv. 1890 no. 8643

14. RIDOLFO DEL GHIRLANDAIO
St. Zanobius revives a boy
c. 1516
Oil on wood
219×193 cm
Inv. 1890 no. 1584

15. FRANCIABIGIO
*Madonna with Child, St. Joseph
and the infant St. John*
1508-1510
Oil on wood
diameter 128 cm
Inv. 1890 no. 888

16. FRA BARTOLOMEO
The Prophet Isaiah
1514-1516
Oil on wood
200×140 cm
Inv. 1890 no. 1448

A. CULLIFORD & C.
for **LONGMAN AND BRODERIP**
"English" harpsichord
London, 1785
Inv. Cherubini 1988/100

17. FRA BARTOLOMEO
The Prophet Job
1514-1516
Oil on wood
200×138,5 cm
Inv. 1890 no. 1449

In the center of the room:

18. GIAMBOLOGNA
Rape of the Sabine women
1582
Plaster cast
Height 410 cm
Sculptures Inv. no. 1071,
Dep. 148

8

PIETRO PERUGINO
Assumption of the Virgin

This altarpiece was located on the high altar of the church in the Benedictine Monastery of Vallombrosa. Perugino painted it with a expert technique using structures and drawings already tested on other, similar great compositions, and dwelling in his usual pleasant way on the decorative details like the Archangel Michael's sophisticated armour on the extreme right.

PETRVS·PERVSINVS·PINXIT·A·D·MCCCCC·

9

FILIPPINO LIPPI
AND PIETRO PERUGINO
Deposition

This painting was part of a grand wooden group commissioned by the friars of Santissima Annunziata of Florence. Filippino Lippi began work on it in 1504 and finished the upper part except for the body of Christ; he then died, and the work was completed in 1507 by Perugino who also painted the other panels to be inserted in the complex structure.

10

GIOVANNI ANTONIO SOGLIANI
*Dispute concerning
the Immaculate Conception*

This panel shows the Doctors of the Church gathered around the body of Adam discussing the question of the Immaculate Conception of the Virgin, a theme also depicted in Carlo Portelli's panel. This work belongs to the specific historical period in which the Catholic Church was particularly intent on consolidating the Marian cult against diffusion of the Lutheran heresy.

ANDREA DEL SARTO
*Christ as the Man
of Sorrows*

This fresco was removed in 1810 from the top of the staircase leading to the novitiate in the Santissima Annunziata Monastery in Floren- ce. Despite the poor condition of the work (perhaps also due to the detachment procedure which presented greater risks in that period than today) the figure of the suffering Christ, his pierced hands resting wearily on the stone of the tomb, still expresses the drama of death and pain with great intensity.

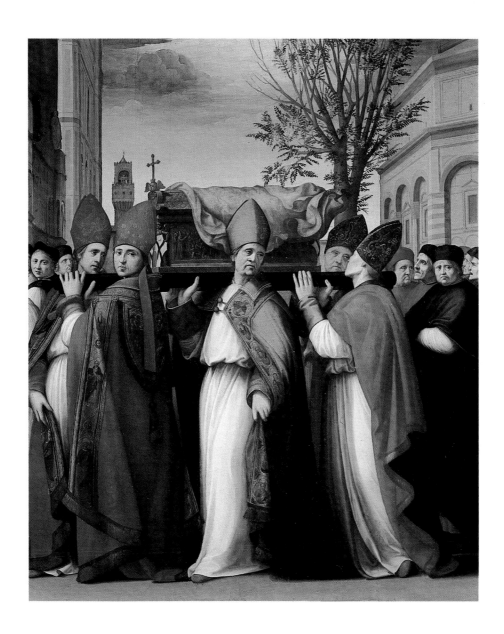

⑫

RIDOLFO DEL GHIRLANDAIO
Removal of the body of St. Zanobius

These two paintings were commissioned in c. 1516 by the Compagnia di San Zanobi, headquartered in the presbytery of Santa Maria del Fiore, to complete the decoration of the altar over which Mariotto Albertinelli's *Annunciation* ⑬ had already been placed in 1510. Since these two paintings were smaller it is probable that they were hung on the side walls of the area housing the altar and probably inserted in architectural frames. The pathetic expressions of the faces, individual and naturalistic, the clear, limpid forms and the essential lines of the composition are distinctive features of Ridolfo's style, which finds its maximum expression here.

The two paintings were transferred from the storage deposit of the Cenacolo di San Salvi to the Accademia Gallery, where they again hang beside Albertinelli's panel.

16-17

FRA BARTOLOMEO
The Prophet Isaiah (on the left)
The Prophet Job (on the right)

These two recently restored panels came from the Billi Chapel in the Basilica of Santissima Annunziata in Florence. At their centre was the *Salvator Mundi and the four Evangelists*, today on show in the Palatina Gallery. Cardinal Carlo

de' Medici purchased the three panels in 1631 and placed them in the Medici house in Piazza San Marco. In 1697 Prince Ferdinand took the central altarpiece to Palazzo Pitti as part of his personal collection, while the two Prophets were passed on to the Uffizi and then to the Accademia. The two Prophets were painted by Fra Bartolomeo immediately after his journey to Rome (c. 1514-1516), and are evidence of his meditations on Michelangelo's Sistine Chapel.

18

GIAMBOLOGNA
Rape of the Sabine women

This is the plaster model for the marble sculptured group which can be seen under Loggia dei Lanzi in Piazza della Signoria. Giambologna's virtuosity here ventures to create for the first time a large-sized marble sculpture with a tightly-knit group of three figures, which almost form a single body, in a circular spiral movement seemingly without beginning or end. When the group was sculpted (1582) it did not have a definite subject but was presented by the artist as a simple exercise in skill; only later was it given the title *Rape of the Sabine women*.

Gallery of the Slaves

The present-day Gallery of the Slaves occupies the area once called the Gallery of Antique Paintings in which, starting from 1817, a great number of Thirteenth and Fourteenth century panel paintings and polyptychs, of unknown attribution and poor state of conservation, were kept. With the arrival of the David and the creation of the Michelangelo Museum the arrangement of the Gallery was radically changed; between the Nineteenth and Twentieth century the hall was dismantled, the Medieval paintings removed, the walls decorated with tapestries and the area dedicated to exhibiting plaster casts of Michelangelo's minor works. In 1909 the Slaves were moved from Buontalenti's Grotto in the Boboli Gardens to the Accademia Gallery, and this hall gradually became a unique collection of the great sculptor's original works. Today the arrangements of the Slaves, along the sides of the Gallery, seems purposely designed to lead the visitor, in a growing crescendo of emotion, to the feet of Michelangelo's colossus.

The works

1. DANIELE DA VOLTERRA
Bust of Michelangelo
c. 1566
Bronze; height 59 cm
Sculptures Inv. no. 1083

2. MICHELANGELO BUONARROTI
Slaves:
The Young Slave
c. 1530
Marble; height 256 cm
Sculptures Inv. no. 1079
Restored: 2001

3. MICHELANGELO BUONARROTI
Slaves:
The Awakening Slave
c. 1530
Marble; height 267 cm
Sculptures Inv. no. 1078
Restored: 2002

4. MICHELANGELO BUONARROTI
St. Matthew
1505-1506
Marble; height 271 cm
Sculptures Inv. no. 1077
Restored: 1997

5. MICHELANGELO BUONARROTI
Slaves:
The Bearded Slave
c. 1530
Marble; height 263 cm
Sculptures Inv. no. 1081
Restored: 1997

6. MICHELANGELO BUONARROTI
Slaves: Atlas
c. 1530
Marble; height 277 cm
Sculptures Inv. no. 1080
Restored: 2002

7. MICHELANGELO BUONARROTI
(ATTRIBUTED TO)
Pietà from Palestrina
(Pietà with St. John the Evangelist)
c. 1547-1559
Marble; height 251 cm
Sculptures Inv. no. 1319

8. MICHELE DI RIDOLFO DEL GHIRLANDAIO
Ideal Portrait
c. 1565
Oil on panel
cm 75,5×57
Inv. 1890 no. 6070
Restored: 2003

9. JACOPO CARUCCI KNOWN AS IL PONTORMO
following cartoon by
MICHELANGELO
Venus and Cupid
c. 1533 (panel);
1532-1533 (cartoon)
Oil on panel
cm 128×194
Inv. 1890 no. 1570
Restored: 2002

10. MICHELE DI RIDOLFO DEL GHIRLANDAIO
Ideal Portrait
(so-called "Zenobia")
c. 1565
Oil on panel
cm 75,5×56
Inv. 1890 n. 6072
Restored: 2003

MICHELANGELO'S *SLAVES*

The four sculptures – exhibited in this room along with other works by Michelangelo and by artists influenced by him – were intended to decorate the base of a complicated mausoleum to be raised in the basilica of St. Peter's in the Vatican as the tomb of Pope Julius II della Rovere. The project had a tormented history and after undergoing radical modifications to reduce the size, the mausoleum was placed in San Pietro in Vincoli where it remains to this day. The four unfinished Slaves not used on the tomb were donated after Michelangelo's death to Grand Duke Cosimo I de' Medici and placed by him in the Buontalenti Grotto in Boboli, from where they were transferred to the Accademia in 1909. The Slaves are a good introduction to an understanding of Michelangelo's unfinished work. Their forms, not brought to a state of perfection, manage to confer a universal meaning on that sensation of an immense struggle to free themselves from the marble vividly perceived by all who view them.

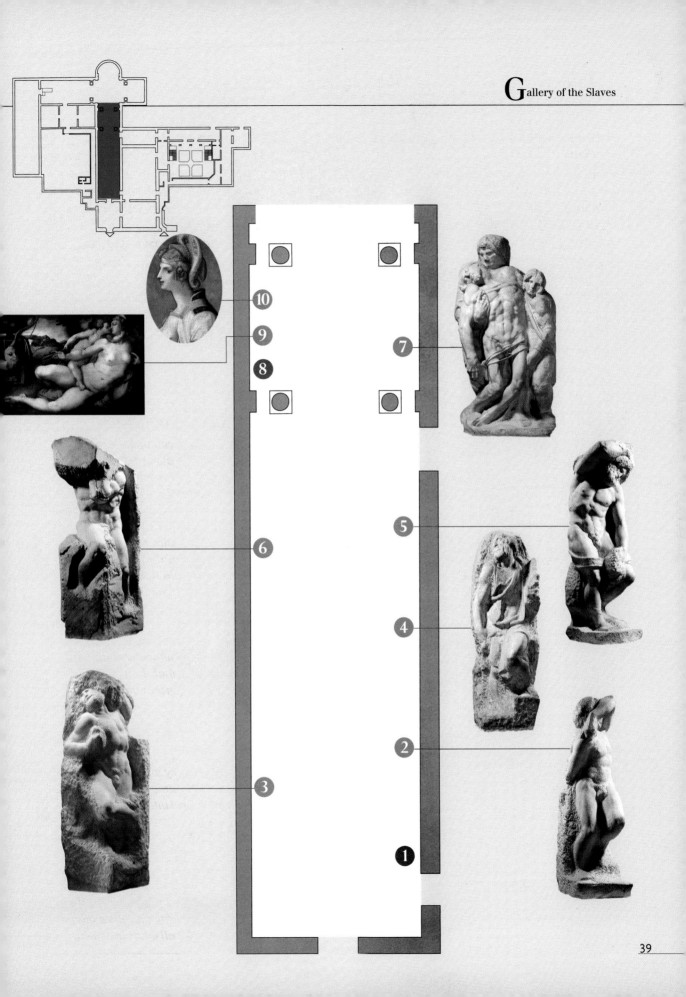

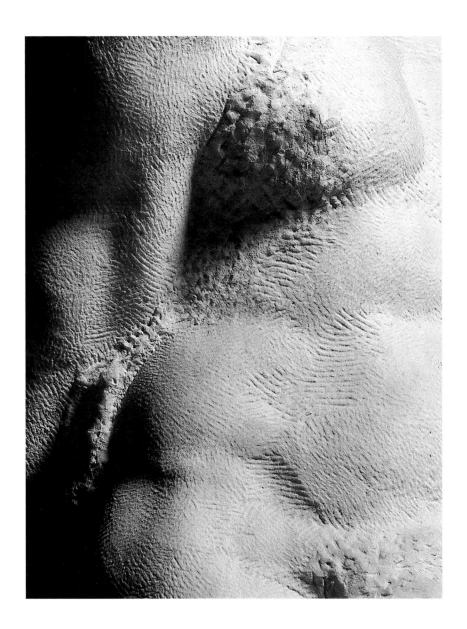

2

MICHELANGELO BUONARROTI
Slaves:
The Young Slave

The first of the four *Slaves* displayed along the walls of the Gallery leading to the Tribuna of *David* is known as *The Young Slave*. He is depicted with slightly bent knees, as if burdened by a weary step, and his left arm is folded across his face, while his right arm slips behind his hip. Emerging from a block of marble which, at the back, seems still untouched, the different parts of the figure itself have been finished to various degrees: the head is roughly outlined, the left side of the torso more finished than the right. However on each part of the surface the marks of the tools used by Michelangelo in his long creative process are still visible.

3

MICHELANGELO BUONARROTI
Slaves:
The Awakening Slave

The powerful limbs of this virile figure struggle to emerge from one side of the imposing block of marble.

The roughly outlined features of the face can barely be made out, and the right leg, bent over the left, protrudes forward to mirror the movement of the right arm.

The result is a tense and dynamic composition which fully expresses the struggle of the material to break out of its own limits.

4

MICHELANGELO BUONARROTI
St. Matthew

The *St. Matthew* was originally to be part of a series of the twelve apostles, a commission given to Michelangelo in 1503 for the columns of Florence Cathedral. In the event the sculptor only worked on one, which is also unfinished, for which reason it was left abandoned in the Opera del Duono (Cathedral Vestry Board) courtyard until 1831. It was moved to the Accademia di Belle Arti where it was first placed in a niche in the courtyard and later, in 1909, in the Gallery near the *Slaves*.

5

MICHELANGELO BUONARROTI
Slaves:
The Bearded Slave

The Bearded Slave is the most nearly finished of the four *Slaves* by Michelangelo .
The face is covered by a thick, curly beard and the thighs are encircled by a strip of cloth. The fine modelling of the torso, the surface finished with soft sensitivity to light and clear evidence of relief modelling, reveals a careful and profound study of anatomy.
The sculpture is traversed below the hips by a fracture, the origin of which is unknown.

45

6

MICHELANGELO BUONARROTI
Slaves: Atlas

This *Slave* is known as *Atlas* because he seems to be carrying a huge weight on his head; however the weight is in fact the head itself, which is not separate and cannot be distinguished. The legs seem to be parted and the bent arms struggle to support the massive weight bearing down on the wide shoulders. *Atlas*, perhaps more than the other *Slaves*, seems to express energy struggling to emerge from the marble.

7

MICHELANGELO BUONARROTI
(ATTRIBUITED TO)
Pietà from Palestrina

Among the large sculptures attributed to Michelangelo Buonarroti, the *Pietà from Palestrina* (c. 1547-1559) is the only one not recorded in the sources or in any document in the archives. It has been in the Accademia since 1939, purchased by the State of Italy from a chapel in Palazzo Barberini at Palestrina.

It was mentioned for the first time as a 'rough draft' by Michelangelo in a historical publication on Palestrina dated 1736. The lack of certain documentation led to a lengthy discussion on its attribution, involving numerous experts, after the presentation of the work in modern times (Garnier 1907).
Many art historians, noting the presence of disproportion, unusual softness of the forms and a certain flatness, have attributed this work to one of the Maestro's followers.

49

9

JACOPO PONTORMO
Venus and Cupid

This work was painted by Jacopo Carrucci, known as Pontormo, around 1533, on a preparatory cartoon drawn by Michelangelo, as can be seen from the sculptural forms of Venus and Cupid.

Presumably soon after having been painted, the nude body of Venus was covered by drapery, since this is how she appears already in the copy made by Vasari, now in Palazzo Colonna in Rome. The painting was restored to its original condition by Ulisse Forni in 1852, revealing Pontormo's nude.

10

MICHELE DI RIDOLFO DEL GHIRLANDAIO
Ideal Portrait (so-called "Zenobia")

Found in the Guardaroba Granducale along with another similar oval portrait displayed in the Galleria, this painting came from the Florentine Convento delle Stabilite, although the subject suggests that it may have been done for a private client. Standing out against a green background Zenobia, with her elaborate coiffeur, her eye seeming to follow the spectator with a courtesan's alluring gaze, shows a close resemblance to a drawing by Michelangelo dating from around 1524.

Tribuna of David

Between 1872 and 1882 the architect Emilio De Fabris designed, in the Accademia Gallery, a hall in the shape of a Latin cross at the center of which, under a circular skylight, the David *would be placed. In early August of 1873 the* David, *sliding on rails through the streets of Florence, was moved to the Accademia. Only in 1882 was work on the Tribuna and the two side wings completed.*

At first copies of Michelangelo's works were exhibited in the side wings. In the early Twentieth century the Michelangelo Museum was dismantled and the walls were decorated with tapestries. It was only in the 1980s that the tapestries were replaced by large paintings by Sixteenth century artists, to emphasize their relationship with Michelangelo's work.

The works

1. MICHELANGELO BUONARROTI
David
1501-1504
Marble
Height 517 cm
Sculptures Inv. no. 1076

1

1

MICHELANGELO BUONARROTI
David

The *David* was originally commissioned by the Florence Opera del Duomo to be placed as a decoration in the Cathedral. It was sculpted by Michelangelo between 1501 and 1504, when it was placed in front of Palazzo Vecchio, following much discussion and debate among the main contemporary Florentine artists. The Giant, as it became known, became a symbol of the civil freedom and virtue of republican Florence, and it remained in its original location until 1873 when it was transferred, using a com-

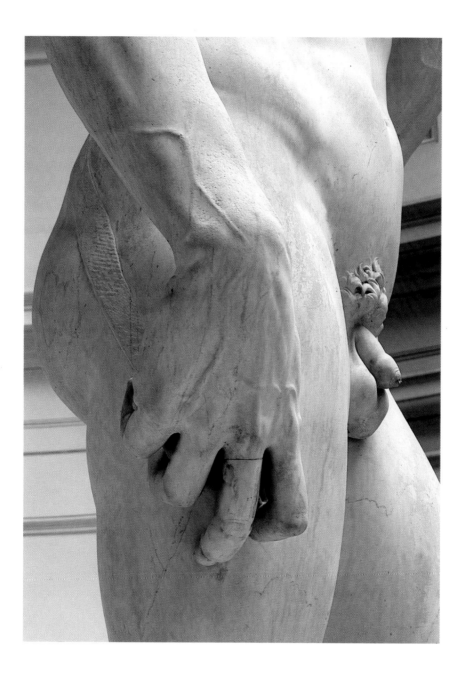

plex support structure resting on wheels, inside the Accademia di Belle Arti, where it can still be admired today.

The sculpture portrays the future king of Israel in a similar form and pose to a triumphant hero of classical Greece. This clearly distances Michelangelo's *David* from those previously made by Donatello and Verrocchio which, adhering more closely to the biblical text, depicted David as a slender boy, unaware of his divine mission.

The statue's perfect modelling, the calm and determined strength of the expression and its imposing size have made it one of the best-known and most admired works of art in the world.

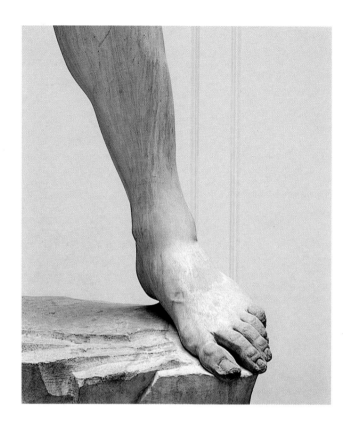

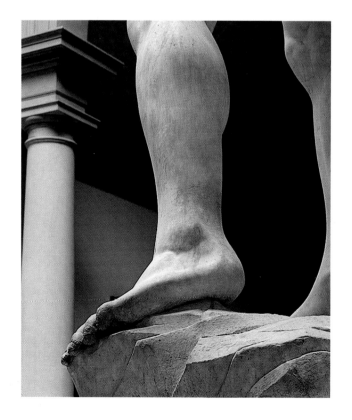

Florentine Fifteenth Century Rooms: A

These rooms are dedicated to Fifteenth century paintings. While some masterpieces are displayed here, like the canvas showing Scenes of Hermit life *by Paolo Uccello and the* Virgin and Child with the infant St. John and two Angels *by Botticelli, the everyday production of the most active studios in Renaissance Florence is also represented. Among these were Ghirlandaio's and Cosimo Rosselli's, where the great masters worked in close contact with assistants and errand boys on the numerous paintings which were to decorate the thousands altars the city's churches, large and small.*

The works

1. ANONYMOUS FLORENTINE
Holy Trinity and Saints
In the predella:
Annunciation
c. 1470-1480
Tempera on wood
220×126 cm
Inv. 1890 no. 3465

2. DOMENICO GHIRLANDAIO
*St. Stephen between
St. James and St. Peter*
1493
Oil on wood
222×222 cm
Inv. 1890 no. 1621

3. DOMENICO DI MICHELINO
Holy Trinity
In the predella:
Stories of Archangels
c. 1460-1470
Tempera on wood
137×79 cm
Inv. 1890 no. 8636

4. NERI DI BICCI (above)
Annunciation
c. 1464
Tempera on wood
188×190 cm
Inv. 1890 no. 8622

**5. MASTER OF THE JOHNSON
NATIVITY AND FILIPPINO LIPPI**
(below))
Annunciation
c. 1460-1470
Tempera on wood; 184×190 cm
Inv. 1890 no. 4632
Restored: 1992

6. DOMENICO DI MICHELINO
*The Archangel Michael
with St. Lawrence
and St. Leonard*
c. 1469
Tempera on wood
171×22,5 cm
Inv. 1890 no. 8621

7. BENOZZO GOZZOLI
*St. Bartholomew,
St. John the Baptist,
St. James the Elder*
c. 1461-1462
Tempera on wood
171×22,5 cm
Inv. 1890 no. 8620

8. DOMENICO DI MICHELINO
(above)
The three Archangels and Tobiolo
c. 1460-1470
Tempera on wood; 183×180 cm
Inv. 1890 no. 8624

9. COSIMO ROSSELLI (below)
*St. Barbara between St. John
the Baptist and St. Matthew*
c. 1470
Tempera on wood
221×221 cm
Inv. 1890 no. 8635
Restored: 2004

**10. PSEUDO PIER FRANCESCO
FLORENTINE** (above)
*The Madonna in adoration
of the Child*
After 1459
Tempera on wood
80×56 cm
Inv. 1890 no. 3158

11. COSIMO ROSSELLI (below)
*Noah and king David
Moses and Abraham*
c. 1460
Tempera on wood
31×66 cm (each)
Inv. 1890 nos. 8632, 8633

**12. MASTER
OF THE CASTELLO NATIVITY**
Nativity
In the predella: *Four Prophets*
c. 1460
Tempera on wood; 213×98 cm
Inv. Deposits no. 171

13. ALESSO BALDOVINETTI (above)
*Holy Trinity and Saints
(Benedict and Giovanni Gualberto)*
c. 1472
Tempera on wood
255×300 cm
Inv. 1890 no. 8637
Restored: 2004

14. LO SCHEGGIA (below)
*Wedding procession
or Cassone (Chest) Adimari*
c. 1450
Tempera on wood
88,5×303 cm
Inv. 1890 no. 8457
Restored: 1990

**15. GIOVAN FRANCESCO
DA RIMINI**
St. Vincenzo Ferreri
In the predella:
*Three scenes from
the life of the Saint*
Mid-xv century
Tempera on wood
191×71 cm
Inv. 1890 no. 3461

16. ANDREA DI GIUSTO
*Madonna with Child, two Angels
and Christ as the Man of Sorrows*
First decades of the xv century
Tempera on wood
103×50 cm
Inv. 1890 no. 6004

**17. DOMENICO DI MICHELINO
AND WORKSHOP** (above)
Madonna with Child and Saints
c. 1460-1470
Tempera on wood
194×202 cm
Inv. 1890 no. 3450

18. ANDREA DI GIUSTO (below)
*Madonna of the Girdle
and Saints*
In the predella:
*Martyrdom of St. Catherine,
Death of the Virgin*
and *Stigmata of St. Francis*
1437
Tempera on wood
210×220 cm
Inv. 1890 no. 3236

19. ANDREA DI GIUSTO
*Madonna with Child
and two Angels*
First half of the xv century
Tempera on wood
117,5×59,5 cm
Inv. 1890 no. 3160

20. MARIOTTO DI CRISTOFANO
*Scenes from the Lives of Christ
and of the Virgin*
In the cuspids:
Annunciation
and *Assumption of the Virgin*
c. 1450-1457
Tempera on wood
263,5×184 cm
Inv. 1890 no. 8508
Restored: 2004

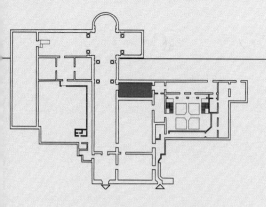

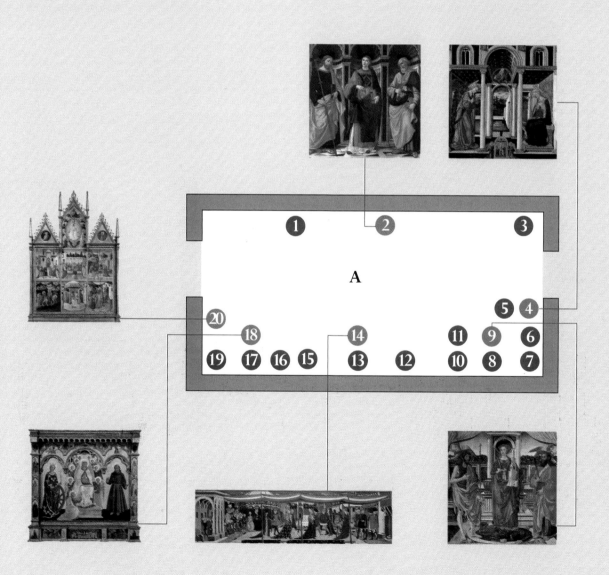

A

2

DOMENICO GHIRLANDAIO
St. Stephen between
St. James and St. Peter

In the past this panel was attributed to Sebastiano Mainardi, a pupil of Ghirlandaio, but it was recently recognised as work of the master himself. A few years after it was painted, perhaps in 1513, the figure of St. Stephen was repainted to look like St. Jerome, by the hand of Fra Bartolomeo, according to traditional accounts. Nineteenth century restoration work then cancelled this modification. In this composition the touch of Ghirlandaio, noted for his lively narrative and decorative elements, is conspicuous in the unusual majesty of the three sculptural figures which strikingly emerge from the "chiaroscuro" effect of the niches.

4

NERI DI BICCI
Annunciation

This panel comes from the Church of Santa Maria del Sepolcro, known as "delle Campora", for which it was commissioned in 1464 by Agnolo Vettori, an outstanding figure in Fifteenth century Florentine politics, several times prior and gonfalonier of the Republic in 1458. Heir to an ancient Florentine studio, founded by his grandfather Lorenzo di Bicci and continued by his father,

Bicci di Lorenzo, Neri di Bicci often reproduced traditional compositions over the years with his impeccable technique, making only the slightest modifications. Worthy of note in this *Annunciation* is the detail of the small board at the bottom showing the *Crucifixion*, and the complex architecture where the deep perspective leads the gaze to the landscape in the background.

9

COSIMO ROSSELLI
St. Barbara between
St. John the Baptist and St. Matthew

Cosimo Rosselli, head of a well-equipped, active family-run studio, painted this gorgeous panel for the Chapel of St. Barbara and St. Quiricus in the Basilica of Santissima Annunziata in Florence. This chapel belonged to the so-called "Teutonic Nation", i.e. to the Germans and Flem-ings. St. Barbara was the patron saint of artillery and therefore she is holding up the tower as a symbol of a line of fortification and crushing a conquered warrior beneath her feet. The composition of the painting (c. 1470) recalls details from works by other contemporary Florentine artists, like Pollaiuolo's panel for the Portuguese cardinal's Chapel in San Miniato and Ghirlandaio's fresco in the Church of Sant'Andrea in Cercina, and it is painted with skill and dignity.

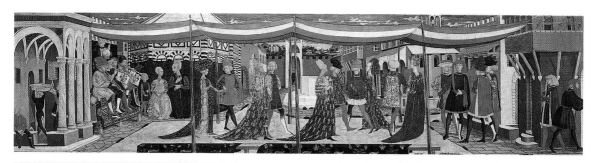

14

LO SCHEGGIA
Wedding procession
or *Cassone (Chest) Adimari*

This was originally listed as *Cassone Adimari* because it was thought to be the front panel of a wedding chest belonging to the Adimari family. The painting (c. 1450) was later recognised as part of a "spalliera", a wall decoration, and was attributed to Giovanni di Ser Giovanni, known as Lo Scheggia, the brother of Masaccio. The images depicted here concern a wedding feast and portray the streets, monuments (the Baptistry can be seen on the left), landscapes and customs of Renaissance Florence with vivacity and extraordinary wealth of detail.

18

ANDREA DI GIUSTO
*Virgin of the Girdle
and Saints*

This painting, dated 1437 and signed "Andrea
de Florentia", comes from the Church of Santa
Margherita in Cortona, and is the work of a painter
active during the first half of the 15th century. The
artist is clearly familiar with the great "modern"
painters, such as Paolo Uccello and Beato Angelico, but solidly linked to the Gothic tradition, as
this altarpiece shows in its use of gold-leaf background and the division of the space into three.

MARIOTTO DI CRISTOFANO
*Scenes from the Lives
of Christ and of the Virgin*

This painting, dated from 1450-1457, coming from the Church of Sant'Andrea a Doccia (a village near Pontassieve, Florence), is made up of six panels portraying *Scenes from the Christ' childhood and from his Life*, the *Death of the Virgin*, and in the large central cusp, the *Assumption*.

The polyptych was attributed in the Nineteenth century to the school of Beato Angelico and subsequently to an artist influenced by Bicci di Lorenzo. In the 1960s it was noticed that similarities existed between this painting and the dual-face panel, present in the same room, representing the *Mystic marriage of St. Catherine of Alexandria* and the *Resurrection of Christ*, painted in 1445 by Mariotto di Cristofano, an artist whose style shows the influence of Beato Angelico and Masolino.

Florentine Fifteenth Century Rooms: B-C

The works

1. NERI DI BICCI
St. Jerome, the Bishop Saint,
St. Francis, St. Philip,
St. Catherine of Alexandria
c. 1444-1453
Tempera on wood
130×89 cm
Inv. 1890 no. 3470

2. PIETRO PERUGINO (?) (above)
The Visitation
c. 1472-1473
Tempera on wood
32×34 cm
Inv. 1890 no. 8654

3. JACOPO DEL SELLAIO (below)
Christ deposed in the Sepulchre
1480-1490
Tempera on wood
44×49 cm
Inv. 1890 no. 8655

4. FRANCESCO BOTTICINI
St. Andrew in adoration
of the Cross
1475-1499
Tempera on wood
73,5×55 cm
Inv. 1890 no. 8656

5. GHERARDO DI GIOVANNI
Madonna in adoration of the Child
with the infant St. John
1475-1480
Tempera on wood; 112,5×61,5 cm
Inv. 1890 no. 8634

6. PAOLO UCCELLO
Scenes of Hermit life
(or "Thebaid")
c. 1460
Tempera on canvas; 83×118 cm
Inv. 1890 no. 5381

7. BIAGIO D'ANTONIO (above)
Announcing Angel,
Eternal Father and
Our Lady of the Annunciation
c. 1475
Tempera on wood; 39×121 cm
Inv. 1890 no. 8619
Restored: 1987

8. SEBASTIANO MAINARDI (below)
Christ as the Man of Sorrows
between the Virgin
and St. John the Evangelist
1475-1500
Tempera on wood; 97×71 cm
Inv. 1890 no. 8623

9. ANONYMOUS FLORENTINE (above)
Annunciation
c. 1490
Tempera on wood; 21×58 cm
Inv. 1890 no. 8639

10. ANONYMOUS FLORENTINE
(below)
Martyrdom of St. Lawrence
c. 1480
Tempera on wood; 65×48 cm
Inv. 1890 no. 6186

11. FRANCESCO BOTTICINI
St. Augustine
1471
Oil on wood
171×51 cm
Inv. 1890 no. 8625

12. COSIMO ROSSELLI
(WORKSHOP OF)
Madonna with Child
crowned by two Angels
c. 1470-1490
Tempera on wood
200×144 cm
Inv. 1890 no. 3205

13. SANDRO BOTTICELLI
Madonna and Child with the
infant St. John and two Angels
c. 1468
Tempera on wood
98×97 cm
Inv. 1890 no. 3166

14. SANDRO BOTTICELLI
AND ASSISTANTS
Madonna with Child
and Saints
1480-1500
Tempera on canvas
203,5×210 cm
Inv. 1890 no. 4344

15. SANDRO BOTTICELLI (?)
Virgin of the Sea
c. 1475-1480
Oil on wood
60,5×49,5 cm
Inv. 1890 no. 8456

16. FILIPPINO LIPPI
St. John the Baptist
St. Mary Magdalene
c. 1496
Oil on wood
136×56 cm (each)
Inv. 1890 nos. 8653, 8651

17. ANONYMOUS FLORENTINE
(above)
Eternal Father
c. 1500-1510
Tempera on wood
67×134 cm
Inv. 1890 no. 8631

18. BARTOLOMEO DI GIOVANNI
(below)
St. Francis receiving the stigmata
Deposition
St. Girolamo
c. 1500-1510
Tempera on wood
35×59,5; 34,5×62; 35×59,5 cm
Inv. 1890 nos. 8629, 8628, 8627
Restored: 1988

19. RAFFAELLINO DEL GARBO
Christ rising from the Sepulchre
c. 1500-1505
Oil on wood
270×290,5 cm
Inv. 1890 no. 8363

20. JACOPO DEL SELLAIO
Deposition and Saints
c. 1491-1494
Tempera on wood
196×200 cm
Inv. 1890 no. 5069

21. LORENZO DI CREDI
Adoration of the Child
c. 1496-1500
Tempera on wood
156×148,5 cm
Inv. 1890 no. 8661
Restored: 1988

22. GHERARDO DI GIOVANNI
Enthroned Madonna
with Child and saints
c. 1480-1495
Tempera on wood
182×199 cm
Inv. 1890 no. 9149
Restored: 1989-1991

23. MASTER
OF THE FIESOLE EPIPHANY
Coronation of Maria
c. 1470-1475
Tempera on wood
186×127,5 cm
Inv. 1890 no. 490

24. FRANCESCO BOTTICINI
St. Monica
1471
Oil on wood
170,5×52 cm
Inv. 1890 no. 8626

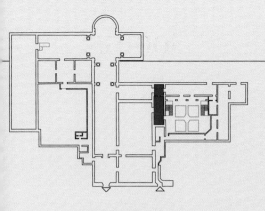

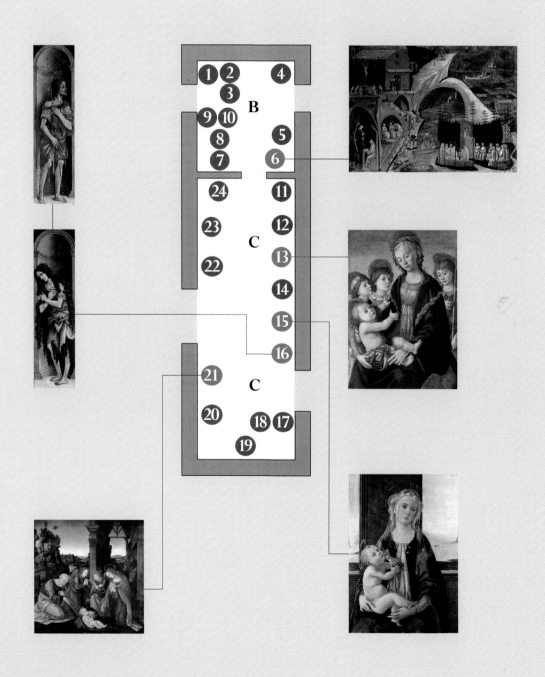

6

PAOLO UCCELLO
Scenes of Hermit life
(or *Thebaid*)

The subject of this painting by Paolo Uccello is not easily interpreted but is certainly linked to a path of meditation and spiritual improvement through prayer. The following episodes can be identified: *The stigmata of St. Francis, St. Jerome worships the Crucifix, The appearance of the Virgin to St. Bernard* and *St. Benedict preaches to his brethren.*

13

SANDRO BOTTICELLI
*Madonna and Child
with the infant St. John and two Angels*

This work, from Botticelli's early phase, the clearly shows the stylistic characteristics of Filippo Lippi, in whose studio Sandro Botticelli was still training. This composition with its diffuse structure was to be very successful in later years and was repeated in numerous terracotta bas-reliefs for private devotional use.

15

SANDRO BOTTICELLI (?)
Madonna of the Sea

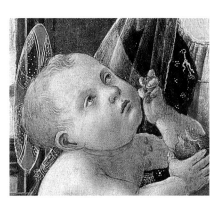

This small panel (c. 1475-1480), which owes its name to the dim seascape in the background, has always been one of the most admired works by visitors to the Gallery.

However the critics are still not in agreement over the attribution, vacillating between Botticelli and Filippino Lippi.

FILIPPINO LIPPI
St. John the Baptist
St. Mary Magdalene

These two paintings (c. 1496) were the side panels of an altarpiece having at the center a *Crucifixion with the Virgin and St. Francis* with gold-leaf background, originally placed in the Chapel of Francesco Valori in San Procolo.

The panels were divided in the mid-Eighteenth century and the central one was destroyed in Berlin in 1945 during World War II.

The two figures in the side panels, St. John the Baptist, consumed by repentance in the desert, and St. Mary Magdalene, are marked by the suffering of spiritual torment, emphasized by their emaciated appearance, tangled hair, torn clothing and bare feet.

In these figures Filippino revived the figurative tradition of the early Fifteenth century, especially as exemplified in polychrome wooden sculptures, to suggest the devout objective of art according to the dictates of the client Valori, one of Girolamo Savonarola's most important followers.

21

LORENZO DI CREDI
Adoration of the Child

The original location of this painting by Lorenzo di Credi is uncertain, some experts believing it to come from the Convento dell'Annunzia-ta, others from the Convento delle Murate. Painted slightly later than the better known *Adoration* in the Uffizi Gallery (c. 1480-1485), it dates to the last decade in the Fifteenth century, a period in which Renaissance style was undergoing dissolution.

Lorenzo di Credi assimilated Leonardo's innovations (both were pupils of Verrocchio) up to the point where they represented a break with the past. In this painting the symmetrical scheme, the view scaled plane by plane, and the sentimental effects of the figures testify to Lorenzo's rejection of Leonardo's perspective studies as well as his links to Fifteenth century tradition. In the landscape in the background and the small figures of shepherds at the left, the quality of the painting is reminiscent of Piero di Cosimo.

Side wings of the Tribuna

Since the beginning of the 1980s this area has housed a series of works by artists who were contemporaries of Michelangelo, or slightly later. Among these are some of Alessandro Allori's large panels.

The works

1. GIULIANO BUGIARDINI
*Madonna and Child
with the Young St John the Baptist*
(or *Madonna della Palma*)
1520
Oil on wood
118,5×91 cm
Inv. 1890 no. 3121
Restored: 2003

2. STEFANO PIERI
Sacrifice of Isaac
1585
Oil on canvas
240,5×162 cm
Inv. 1890 no. 2133
Restored: 2003

**3. PIER FRANCESCO
DI JACOPO FOSCHI**
*Holy Family with the
Young St John the Baptist*
1525-1535
Oil on wood
105×87 cm
Inv. no. 235 blue-no. 302 yellow
Restored: 2003

**4. TOMMASO MANZUOLI KNOWN AS
MASO DA SAN FRIANO**
Allegory of Fortitude
1560-1562
Oil on wood
178×142 cm
Inv. 1890 no. 8024
Restored: 2003

5. CARLO PORTELLI
Immaculate Conception
1566
Oil on wood
415×246,2 cm
Inv. 1890 no. 4630
Restored: 2003

**6. VASARIAN PAINTER
FROM GIORGIO VASARI (?)**
St. Barbara
1550-1560
Oil on canvas
198×155 cm
Inv. 1890 no. 5868
Restored: 2003

**7. FRANCESCO MORANDINI
KNOWN AS IL POPPI**
Allegory of Charity
1575-1580
Oil on wood
130×101,5 cm
Inv. 1890 no. 9287
Restored: 2003

**8. TOMMASO MANZUOLI KNOWN AS
MASO DA SAN FRIANO**
*The Trinity and Saints
James the Great, Augustine,
Philip and Crispinus*
1569-1570
Oil on wood

294,3×171 cm
Inv. 1890 no. 2118
Restored: 2003

**9. FRANCESCO DE' ROSSI
KNOWN AS IL SALVIATI**
*Madonna and Child,
Young St John the Baptist
and an Angel*
1543-1548
Oil on wood
103×79,5 cm
Inv. 1890 no. 6065
Restored: 2003

**10. AGNOLO DI COSIMO TORI
KNOWN AS IL BRONZINO**
Deposition
1560-1561
Oil on wood
349×254 cm
Inv. 1890 no. 3491
Restored: 2003

11. ALESSANDRO ALLORI
*Madonna enthroned
with the Christ Child, the Young
St John the Baptist and Saints
Lucia, Cecilia, Agnes, Apollonia,
Catherine, Elizabeth
and Allegorical figures
of Active and Contemplative Life*
1575
Oil on wood
413×289 cm
Inv. 1890 no. 3182
Restored: 2003

12. ALESSANDRO ALLORI
Annunciation
1578-1579
Oil on wood
446×282 cm
Inv. 1890 no. 8662
Restored: 2003

13. ALESSANDRO ALLORI
Coronation of the Virgin
1593
Oil on canvas
mounted on wood
416×285,2 cm
Inv. 1890 no. 3171
Restored: 2003

14. ALESSANDRO ALLORI
Baptism of Christ
c. 1589
Oil on wood
168,5×99,5 cm
Inv. 1890 no. 2175
Restored: 2003

15. COSIMO GAMBERUCCI
*St Peter Healing
the Lame Man*
1599
Oil on wood
409,5×260,5 cm
Inv. 1890 no. 4631
Restored: 2003

16. ALESSANDRO ALLORI
Annunciation
1603
Oil on canvas
162×103,5 cm
Inv. Castello no. 494
and Inv. Deposits no. 131
Restored: 2003

17. STEFANO PIERI
Deposition of Christ
1587
Oil on wood
171×131 cm
Inv. 1890 no. 1595
Restored: 2003

18. SANTI DI TITO
*Entrance of Christ
into Jerusalem*
1582-1583
Oil on wood
349,3×227 cm
Inv. 1890 no. 8667
Restored: 2003

19. SANTI DI TITO
*Lamentation over Christ
with Saints John the Baptist,
Catherine of Alessandria
and the donor*
c. 1592
Oil on wood
198,5×163,5 cm
Inv. 1890 no. 4637
Restored: 2003

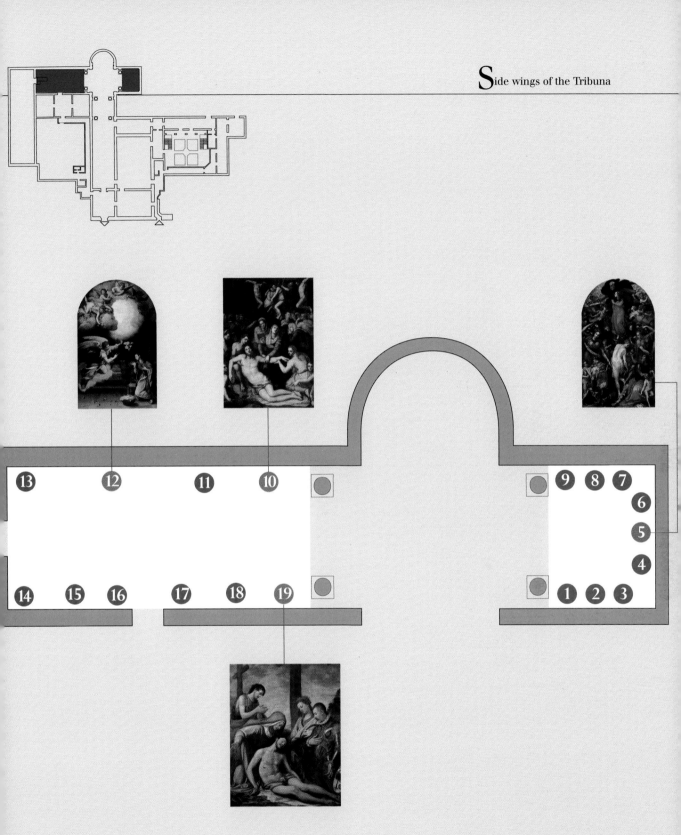

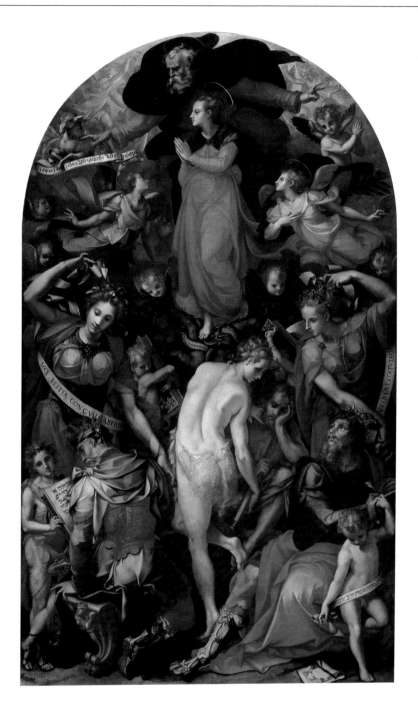

5

CARLO PORTELLI
Immaculate Conception

The painting, whose recent restoration has revived its brilliant colors and clear legibility, revealing the splendid nude Eve, was commissioned for the Church of Ognissanti in Florence. Its subject is the Immaculate Conception of Mary, a theme originating in the second half of the 15th century, but long subjected to heated debate within the Catholic Church. Portelli's strongly Mannerist style is exemplified here in the space entirely concentrated in the foreground, and in the sinuous poses of his figures, in studied contrast to one another.

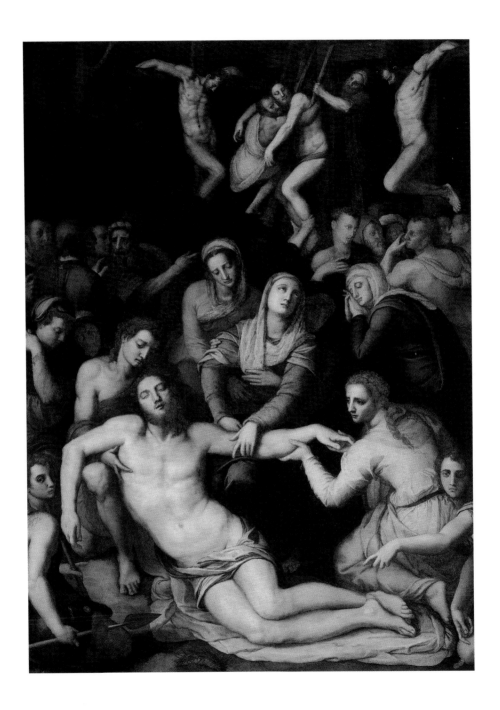

10

AGNOLO BRONZINO
Deposition

This enormous painting was commissioned by Cosimo I de' Medici for the Church of the Observant Minorites at Portoferraio, (Island of Elba, where it arrived transported by ship down the Arno. At the far left, above, the bearded old man in the background is a self-portrait of the artist. Although the work survived in a deplorable state of conservation, due to a devastating fire that broke out in the church, a recent difficult, lengthy restoration has revealed again its significant artistic merit.

12

ALESSANDRO ALLORI
Annunciation

This panel, restored in 2003, was commissioned by Sister Laura de' Pazzi for the Convent of Montedomini, in whose church it was situated when the holy institution was suppressed and its furnishings confiscated by the State. The severe and contained composition, suitable for a convent in a time of Counter-reform, is softened by the charming still-life of the basket with clothes and the delicate flowers scattered on the floor.

19

SANTI DI TITO
Lamentation for Christ

This painting, which comes from the chapel in Fortezza da Basso (Florence), portrays Christ taken down from the cross, surrounded by the Virgin, Saint John the Baptist, Saint Catherine and the donor wearing ornate armor with the insignia of the Knights of Saint Stephen, recently identified, on the basis of the coat-of-arms clearly visible at his side, as Ernando Sastri of Spain. The particular sensitivity to color, clearly revealed by the restoration 2003, seems to indicate a dating around the 1590s, a period in which Titi was strongly influenced by the colorism of Cigoli.

Nineteenth Century Room

The large Nineteenth Century Room was conceived and realised in order to provide the collection of plaster casts by Lorenzo Bartolini with a stable and definitive location. However the intention was also to offer the visitor tangible evidence of the Nineteenth century academic origins of this Gallery, today mainly known for Michelangelo's David.

A. The sculptures

1. LORENZO BARTOLINI
Funerary Monument to Elisa Baciocchi
1820
Plaster model; height 211 cm;
Sculptures Inv. no. 1181, n. 1256 (bas-relief)

2. LORENZO BARTOLINI
*Portrait of the Irish poetess
Lady Mary Tighe*
c. 1820
Plaster model; height 139 cm
Sculptures Inv. no. 1207

3. LORENZO BARTOLINI
Portrait of a Young Girl
1820-1825
Plaster model; height 101 cm
Sculptures Inv. no. 1223

4. LORENZO BARTOLINI
Emma and Julia Campbell
1819-1820
Plaster model; height 157 cm
Sculptures Inv. no. 1183

5. LORENZO BARTOLINI
Titian's Venus
c. 1821
Plaster model; height 61 cm
Sculptures Inv. no. 1313

6. LORENZO BARTOLINI
Grape harvester
1816-1820
Plaster model; height 133 cm
Sculptures Inv. no. 1216

7. LORENZO BARTOLINI
Venus
c. 1817
Plaster model; height 158 cm
Sculptures Inv. no. 1213

8. LORENZO BARTOLINI
Tethys caressing Jove
c. 1817
Plaster model; height 25 cm (male head), height 56 cm (female bust)
Sculptures Inv. no. 1426

9. LORENZO BARTOLINI
Jean Auguste Dominique Ingres
c. 1817
Plaster model for a monument
in bronze: Paris, École des Beaux-Arts;
diameter 23 cm.; Sculptures Inv. no. 1427

10. LORENZO BARTOLINI
Justice protecting Innocence
c. 1817
Relief sculpture in plaster; height 62 cm
Sculptures Inv. no. 1304

11. LORENZO BARTOLINI
*Portrait of Frances Ann Vane-Tempest,
Marchioness of Londonberry,
with her son George*
c. 1823
Plaster model for a marble monument:
Tresside, Wynyand Park;
height 165 cm.; Sculptures Inv. no. 1205

12. LORENZO BARTOLINI
Charity as Educator
1817-1824
Plaster model for a marble monument:
Florence, Galleria Palatina; height 181 cm.; Sculptures Inv. no. 1182

13. LORENZO BARTOLINI
*Portrait of Anne Lullin
de Chateaurieux,
wife of Eynard*
1812
Plaster model for a marble monument:
Genève, Palais Eynard
height 175 cm.; Sculptures Inv. no. 1206

14. LORENZO BARTOLINI
Juno
1823-1830
Plaster model; height 180 cm
Sculptures Inv. no. 1202

15. LORENZO BARTOLINI
*Allegorical figures
for the Demidoff Monument*
1828-1850:

The Gratitude
Plaster model; height 106 cm
Sculptures Inv. no. 1209

The Charity
Plaster model; height 190 cm
Sculptures Inv. no. 1175

*Nature unveiling
herself to Art*
Plaster model; height 220 cm
Sculptures Inv. no. 1176

The Gratitude
Plaster cast; height 108 cm
Sculptures Inv. no. 1221

The Muse of Festivities
Plaster model; height 190 cm
Sculptures Inv. no. 1177

The Siberia
Plaster model; height 220 cm
Sculptures Inv. no. 1174

16. LORENZO BARTOLINI
*Praying figure
for the monument to Pietro Recchi*
1836
Plaster model for a marble monument:
Ferrare, Cimetière
monumental; height 162 cm.
Sculptures Inv. no. 1251

17. LORENZO BARTOLINI
The vow of innocence
c. 1848
Plaster cast height 154 cm.
Sculptures Inv. no. 1211

18. LORENZO BARTOLINI
Beatrice Donati
1846
Plaster cast; height 165 cm
Sculptures Inv. no. 1212

19. LORENZO BARTOLINI
Niccolò Machiavelli
1845-1846
Plaster model; height 210 cm
Sculptures Inv. no. 1201

20. LUIGI PAMPALONI
*Relief sculpture
for the monument to Luciano
Bonaparte, Prince of Canino*
1840-1847
Plaster model; height 219 cm
Sculptures Inv. nos. 1244, 1243

21. LORENZO BARTOLINI
Bacchante
1834
Plaster model; Length 154 cm
Sculptures Inv. no. 1204

22. LORENZO BARTOLINI
Nymph of the Scorpion
Before 1837
Plaster model; height 80 cm
Sculptures Inv. no. 1222

23. LORENZO BARTOLINI
Nymph of the Serpent
Before 1840
Plaster model; height 121 cm
Sculptures Inv. no. 1203

24. LUIGI PAMPALONI
Filippo Brunelleschi
1827-1830
Plaster model
for a marble monument:
Florence, Piazza del Duomo
height 135 cm.; Sculptures Inv. no. 1231

25. LUIGI PAMPALONI
Arnolfo di Cambio
1827-1830
Plaster model; height 138 cm.
Sculptures Inv. no. 1230

26. LORENZO BARTOLINI
The table of Cupids
Before 1845
Plaster model; diameter 125 cm
Sculptures Inv. no. 1220

27. LUIGI PAMPALONI
*Girl of the turtle-doves
(Innocence)*
1831
Plaster model; height 64 cm
Sculptures Inv. no. 1236

28. LUIGI PAMPALONI
Boy with a dog
1827
Plaster model; height 58 cm
Sculptures Inv. no. 1237

29. LORENZO BARTOLINI
*Fraternal rivalry
(Lady Bingham's sons)*
Ante 1847
Plaster model; height 66 cm
Sculptures Inv. no. 1257

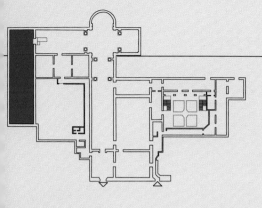

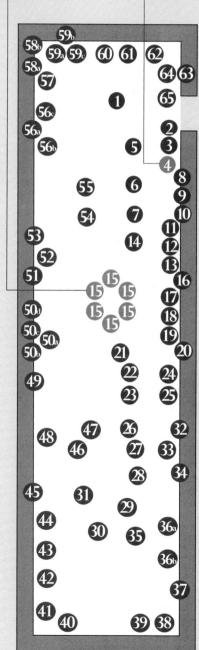

30. LUIGI PAMPALONI
Cupid
1833
Plaster model; height 108 cm
Sculptures Inv. no. 1234

31. LUIGI PAMPALONI
Cupid with a Swan
After 1834
Plaster model; height 86 cm
Sculptures Inv. no. 1232

32. LUIGI PAMPALONI
*Bas-relief for the funerary monument
to Annamaria Frescobaldi*
1842-1844
Plaster model; height 140 cm
Sculptures Inv. no. 1287

33. LUIGI PAMPALONI
Monument to Virginia de Blasis
1839
Plaster model; height 145 cm
Sculptures Inv. no. 1239

34. LUIGI PAMPALONI
*Relief sculpture
for the Tellinson monument*
c. 1840
Plaster model; height 119 cm
Sculptures Inv. no. 1247

35. LORENZO BARTOLINI
Monument to Leon Battista Alberti
After 1838
Plaster model; height 224 cm
Sculptures Inv. no. 1180

36a-b. LUIGI PAMPALONI
Orphans on the cliff
1838-1842
Plaster model for a marble monument:
Pistoia, Istituto Tecnico Fermi; height
71 cm (male), height 76 cm (female)
Sculptures Inv. nos. 1235, 1238

37. LORENZO BARTOLINI
*Monument to Count
Bastiani Brunacci*
c. 1840
Plaster modelfor a marble monument:
Pisa, Camposanto
height 71 cm.; Sculptures Inv. no. 1191

38. LUIGI PAMPALONI
The Penitent Magdalene
c. 1847
Plaster model; height 85 cm
Sculptures Inv. no. 1246

39. FRANCESCO POZZI
Ciparisso
1851
Plaster model; height 117,5 cm
Without Inv.

40. FRANCESCO POZZI
Bacchante with Faunus and panther
1818
Plaster model; height 115 cm
Without Inv.; Gen. Cat. no. 741

41. LUIGI PAMPALONI
Monument to Lazzaro Papi
1835
Plaster model; height 175 cm
Sculptures Inv. nos. 1286 and 1312

42. LUIGI PAMPALONI
*Monument to Maria Radzwill
Krasinski with the son Zygmunt*
1839-1841
Plaster model; 110×200 cm
Sculptures Inv. no. 1241

43. LUIGI PAMPALONI
*Monument to Wanda
Wancowicz Tyskiewicz*
1842-1845
Plaster model; length 196,5 cm;
height 57 and height 52 cm.
Sculptures Inv. nos. 1240, 1248

44. LUIGI PAMPALONI
Reclining girl
1826
Plaster model; height 22 cm
Sculptures Inv. no. 1250

45. LORENZO BARTOLINI
*Medallion for the monument
to Gerolamo Segato*
1838-1844
Plaster cast for a marble monument:
Florence, Santa Croce
diameter 41 cm.; Sculptures Inv. no. 1193

46. LUIGI PAMPALONI
Chloe
1834
Plaster model; height 74 cm
Sculptures Inv. no. 1233

**47. UNKNOWN OF
BARTOLINIAN SCHOOL**
Nymph
c. 1840-1850
Plaster model; height 128 cm
Sculptures Inv. no. 1215

48. LORENZO BARTOLINI
Monument to Sophie Zamoiska
1838-1844
Plaster cast; length 187 cm
Sculptures Inv. no. 1314

49. LORENZO BARTOLINI
*Relief sculpture for a monument
to Caroline Hungher*
1835-1840
Plaster model; height 187 cm
Sculptures Inv. no. 1254

50. LORENZO BARTOLINI
*Monument to Hortense
de Beauharnais*
1838-1845
Plaster model for a marble monument:
Arenberger, Napoleonmuseum; height
131 cm; height 52 cm, height 69 cm,
height 50,5 cm.; Sculptures Inv. nos.
1210, 1302, 1303, 1306

52. LUIGI PAMPALONI
Relief sculpture for a monument to Julie Clary Bonaparte
1846
Plaster model for a marble monument: Florence, Santa Croce height 59 cm.; Sculptures Inv. no. 1245

52. LORENZO BARTOLINI
The inconsolable
1840
Plaster model for a marble funerary monument to Count Giovan Francesco Mastiani Brunacci: Pisa, Camposanto; height 121 cm. Sculptures Inv. no. 1506 (coat-of-arms); no. 1501 (relief sculpture of the Count's profile)

53. LORENZO BARTOLINI
Bas-relief for the monument to Maria Temple Bowdoin
c. 1822
Plaster model for a marble monument: Livorno, Cimitero degli Inglesi; height 104 cm
Sculptures Inv. no. 1252

54. LORENZO BARTOLINI
Cupid
After 1841
Plaster model; height 118 cm
Sculptures Inv. no. 1253

55. LORENZO BARTOLINI
Narcissus
1830-1850
Plaster model; height 179 cm
Sculptures Inv. no. 1218

56a-c. LORENZO BARTOLINI
Monument to Vittorio Fossombroni
1846
Plaster model; height 97 (a), height 174 (b), height 176 (c) cm
Sculptures Inv. nos. 1227, 1228, 1192

57. LORENZO BARTOLINI
Angel for an unknown monument
1830-1850
Plaster model; height 122 cm
Sculptures Inv. no. 1225

58a-b. LORENZO BARTOLINI
Bas-relief for the monument to Louis Guillaume de Cambray-Digny
1844
Plaster model for a marble monument: Parma, Santa Maria della Steccata; height 120 cm. Sculptures Inv. nos. 1255, 1200

59a-c. LORENZO BARTOLINI
Monument to Count Albrecht Adam Neipperg
1829-1841
Plaster model for a marble monument: Florence, Santa Croce; height 42 (a), height 192 (b), height 166 (c) cm.
Sculptures Inv. nos. 1197, 1226, 1258

60. ULISSE CAMBI
Daphnes and Chloe
1854
Plaster model; height 153 cm
Gen. Cat. G.A.M. no. 740

61. ULISSE CAMBI
Aconzio
1835
Plaster model; height 155 cm
Sculptures Inv. no. 1261

62. LORENZO BARTOLINI (above)
Relief sculpture with winged figure
1835; Plaster model; height 53 cm
Sculptures Inv. no. 1289

63. LORENZO BARTOLINI (above)
Relief sculpture with male figure
1835
Plaster model; height 49 cm
Sculptures Inv. no. 1305

64. LORENZO BARTOLINI (below)
Relief sculpture with five figures
1838-1850
Plaster model; height 38,5 cm
Sculptures Inv. no. 1292

65. LORENZO BARTOLINI
Bas-relief for the monument to Henriette Stratford Canning
c. 1818
Modelli in gesso for a marble monument: Losanna, Cathédrale des Anglais; (from right to left and from top to bottom)height 36 cm (diameter); height 63 cm; height 64 cm; height 64 cm; height 63 cm.; Sculptures Inv. nos. 1288, 1291, 1309, 1261, 1508

B. The paintings

66. IRENE DUCLOS PARENTI (above)
Copy of Andrea del Sarto's "Virgin of the Sack"
1775
Oil on canvas; 181×385 cm
Without Inv., A.M.O. d.a. 313

67. LUIGI MUSSINI (below)
Sacred Music
1841
Oil on canvas; 150×104 cm
Acc. Inv. no. 292 [C.G.1]

68. FRANCESCO SABATELLI (above)
Copy of Titian's "Assunta"
1827
Oil on canvas; 250×145 cm
Without Inv.

69. JACOPO PONTORMO (below)
Ward in the San Matteo Hospital
c. 1513-1514
Detached fresco; 100×161 cm
Inv. 1890 no. 9385

70. FRANCESCO NENCI
Oedipus freed from his bindings by a shepherd
1817
Oil on canvas; 218×152 cm
Gen. Cat. no. 5.; Deposits no. 52

71. CESARE MUSSINI
The death of Atala
1830
Oil on canvas; 225×273 cm
Gen. Cat. no. 16

72. ANTONIO PUCCINELLI (above)
An episode from the slaughter of the Innocents
1852
Oil on canvas; 200×145 cm
Gen. Cat. no. 21

73. ANTONIO PUCCINELLI (below)
The Hebrews in Babylonia
1851
Oil on canvas; 67,5×133 cm
Without Inv.

74. GIUSEPPE FATTORI
The Baptist admonishing Herod
1856
Oil on canvas; 282×357 cm
Acc. Inv. no. 461

75. EUGENIO PRATI (above)
Michelangelo to whom Zuccari presents Barocci
1868
Oil on canvas; 174×136 cm
Without Inv.

76. RAFFAELLO SORBI (below)
Death of Corso Donati
1861
Oil on canvas; 136×176 cm
Without Inv.

77. BENEDETTO SERVOLINI
Death of Filippo Strozzi
1833
Oil on canvas; 300×410 cm
Gen. Cat. no. 614

78. DEMOSTENE MACCIÒ
Fra Benedetto da Fojano in prison
c. 1867
Oil on canvas; 147×203 cm
Without Inv.

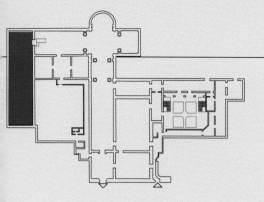

79. BENEDETTO SERVOLINI
Orlando captures a horse
1834
Oil on canvas
300×345 cm
Gen. Cat. no. 613

80. GIUSEPPE COLIGNON
(above)
*The beheading
of the Baptist*
c. 1860
Oil on canvas
103×123 cm
Acc. Inv. no. 338

81. BALDASSARE CALAMAI
(below)
*Dante visiting the Inferno
accompanied by Virgil
recognizes Farinata*
1825
Oil on canvas
191×153 cm
Without Inv.

82. LUIGI MUSSINI (above)
*The giving of alms
according
to evangelical Charity
and according
to worldly Ostentation*
1844
Oil on canvas
116×147 cm
Acc. Inv. no. 383

83. SILVESTRO LEGA
(below)
*David calms Saul's
fury with the harp*
1852
Oil on canvas
133×174 cm
Without Inv.

84. LEOPOLDO NEOFRESCHI
(above)
*Alessandro Magno
about to drink
from a poisoned cup*
1794
Oil on canvas
Measurements are not available
Gen. Cat. no.16

85. CESARE MUSSINI
(below)
*Francis I at the bedside
of the dying Leonardo*
1828
Oil on canvas
145×172 cm
G.A.M. Dep. no. 53

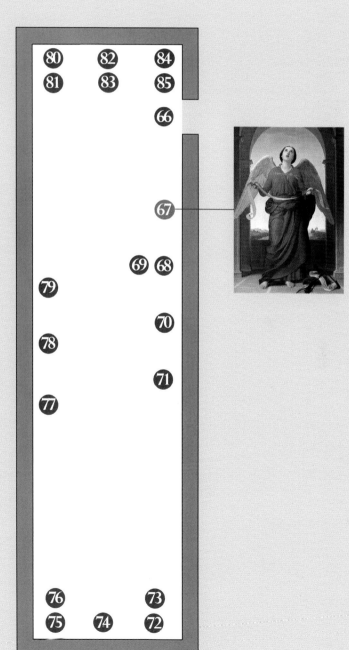

15

LORENZO BARTOLINI
Demidoff Monument

The commemorative monument to count Nikolaj Demidoff was commissioned by his sons Paul and Anatolij in 1828, on the death of their father. Several times interrupted and restarted when the difficulties were overcome, it was only placed where it stands today (in Piazza Demidoff, opposite Lungarno Serristori, in Florence) in 1871. The work was finished by Romanelli, a pupil of Bartolini who took over his workshop. It was a grand and complex project, consisting of many statues, some larger than life, with complicated allegorical meaning. The plaster model of the central group, depicting the count Nikolaj with his son Anatolij, has been lost.

4

LORENZO BARTOLINI
Emma and Julia Campbell

A visit to Bartolini's studio by Lady Barry, an English author who admired his work, procured the artist several commissions from the British aristocracy. Among these was the portrait of the Campbell sisters portrayed in the act of dancing commissioned by their mother Lady Charlotte Campbell, whom the artist met in Florence between September of 1819 and August of 1820. The marble original is thought to be in the dining room of the Inveraray Castle, the property of the Duke of Argyll in Scotland. Although this work is still dominated by neo-classical taste, it reveals Bartolini's early purist orientation during these years. The two girls are portrayed "in antique style", wearing sandals and classical tunics bound under the breast by narrow ribbons. On this group traces of the so-called "dots" procedure, used to mark the angles and the various depths of the points to be reproduced on the block of marble, can be detected.

67

LUIGI MUSSINI
Sacred Music

This is one of the pictures which testify to the original bond between the Accademia Gallery and the School of Accademia delle Belle Arti. Luigi Mussini painted it in Rome in 1841 as an trial for his academic pension. In that same year it was exhibited in the Prize-winners Gallery of the Florence Accademia, where it remained for years.

The picture represents a youth with wings gazing upward toward heaven, her lips parted in a liturgical chant. *Sacred Music* is a clear and illustrious example of Purism in Tuscany, and of how Luigi Mussini shared in the experience of the Nazarenes who drew inspiration from great examples of Fifteenth and Sixteenth centuries painting.

Luigi Mussini had also the chance to learn stylistic rigor in drawing directly from Ingres, who stayed in Florence for some time in the 1820s.

Thirteenth and Early Fourteenth C. Room

The Florentine Gothic painting route (in three rooms) starts in this room, which house many gold-leaf background panels in an absolutely unique collection of its kind. Displayed in the central room are works by artists predating Giotto or his contemporaries, like the Master of San Gaggio and Pacino di Buonaguida; in the right-hand room are Giotto's direct followers, Taddeo Gaddi, Bernardo Daddi, Jacopo del Casentino; in the left-hand room are the Orcagnas and their close collaborators.

The works

1. **GUIDO DA SIENA**
Enthroned Madonna and Child
c. 1265-1270
Tempera on wood
125×73 cm
Inv. 1890 no. 435

2. **FLORENTINE PAINTER**
Painted Cross, with Mary Magdalene worshipping at the feet of Jesus
1285-1290
Tempera on wood
296×197 cm
Inv. 1890 no. 1345

3. **FLORENTINE PAINTER**
Enthroned Madonna and Child
1250 1260
Tempera on wood; 94×41,5
Inv. 1890 no. 5033
Restored: 2000

4. **PACINO DI BUONAGUIDA**
Christ crucified between the grieving Virgin and St. John
c. 1315-1320
Tempera on wood; 190×249 cm
Inv. 1890 no. 8568

5. **PACINO DI BUONAGUIDA**
The Tree of Life
1310-1315
Tempera on wood; 248×170 cm
Inv. 1890 no. 8459
Restored: 1982-1985

6. **PACINO DI BUONAGUIDA**
Madonna and Child
c. 1320
Tempera on wood; 80,8×51,2 cm
Inv. 1890 no. 6146

7. **PACINO DI BUONAGUIDA**
St. Vescovus [Nicolas?];
St. John the Evangelist;
St. Vescovus [Proculous?]
1305-1310
Tempera on wood
71×48,2; 70,5×48,4; 70,7×44,7 cm
Inv. 1890 nos. 8698, 8699, 8700
Restored: 2002

8. **MASTER OF THE MAGDALENE**
The St. Magdalene and eight scenes from her life
1280-1285
Tempera on wood; 178×90 cm
Inv. 1890 no. 8466

9. **MASTER OF THE MAGDALENE**
St. John the Evangelist and scenes from his life;
St. James Major and scenes from his life
1290-1295
Tempera on wood
65×64 et 66×60 cm
Deposits Inv. nos. 121, 122

10. **GIOTTO**
Head of Shepherd and herds
1315-1325
Fragment of detached fresco from *Joachim among the shepherds* (?)
250×135 cm
Without Inv.
(from the Church of Badia in Florence)

11. **MASTER OF ST. CECILIA**
Enthroned Madonna and Child
1320-1325
Tempera on wood
185×97 cm
Inv. 1890 no. 5917

12. **MASTER OF THE CORSI CRUCIFIX**
(above)
Painted cross
1310-1315
Tempera on wood
308×229 cm
Inv. 1890 no. 436

13. **GRIFO DI TANCREDI**
Enthroned Madonna with Child and St. Paul, St. Peter, St. John the Baptist, St. John the Evangelist
c. 1300
Tempera on wood
205×115 cm
Inv. 1890 no. 6115
Restored: 1986-1987

14. **PAINTER FROM LUCCA**
Enthroned Madonna with Child and two Angels
1240-1250
Tempera on wood
126×72,5 cm
Inv. 1890 no. 433
Restored: 1988

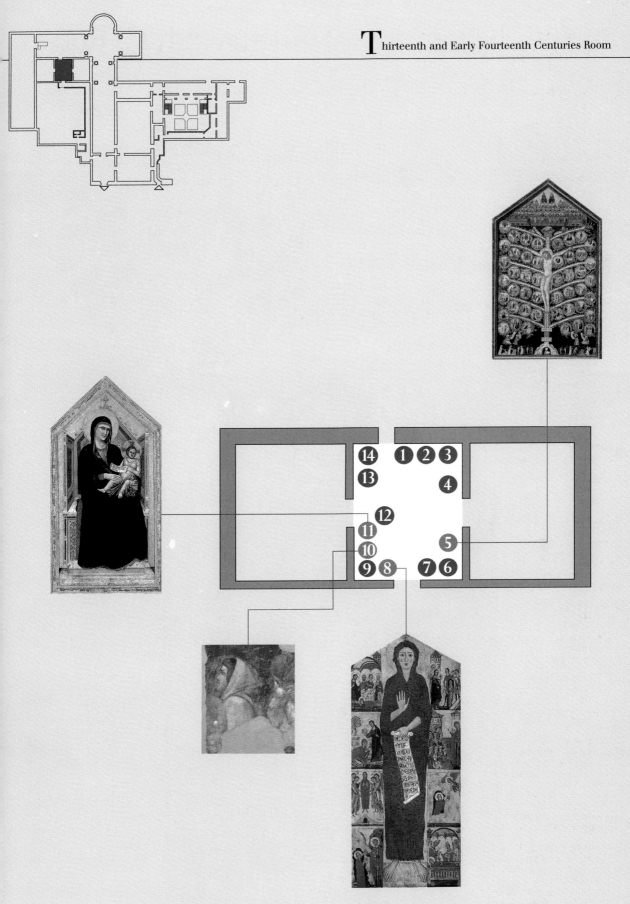

5

PACINO DI BUONAGUIDA
The Tree of Life

With its vivid colours and sophisticated drawing (Pacino was also a famous illuminator), this painting mainly illustrates the content of St. Bonaventure's *Lignum Vitae*, although there are also many scenes and scrolls alluding to biblical texts. In its entirety it appears as a large doctrinal page for meditation as well as an image to be admired. The subject of the illustration is the genealogy of Christ, who is shown nailed to the tree-shaped cross with its roots on a rocky mountain, symbolising Mount Calvary.

8

MASTER OF THE MAGDALENE
*The St. Magdalene
and eight scenes from her life*

This panel, coming from the Convento della SS. Annunziata, clearly exemplifies Florentine painting before Giotto. The Master of the Magdalene set up one of the most productive studio in Florence (1265-1290), and shows evidence of attention to the innovations introduced by Cimabue. In this sense, the small side scenes, which offer a direct and lively narrative of moments from the Saint's life, are more attractive than the solemn central figure. A conspicuous example are the naturalistic landscape elements in the background of the *Noli me tangere* (depicted in the second scene on the left).

10

GIOTTO
Head of Shepherd and herds

This fragment of a detached fresco comes from the ancient high chapel of the Church of Badia in Florence which, according to Ghiberti and other sources earlier than Vasari, was frescoed by Giotto, who also painted the polyptych over the high altar, now in the Uffizi Gallery. In the past this and a few other surviving pictorial fragments were not unanimously accepted by critics as authentic works by Giotto, but in recent years the pictorial quality of this shepherd's head – originally belonging in all probability to the scene of Joachim among the shepherds – has been noted by the greatest scholars of Giotto's art. More than one expert has observed at most a certain stylistic diversity between the Uffizi polyptych, a key work in the development of Giotto's style around the year 1300, and this fragment, whose freshness and luminosity point to a substantially later dating, perhaps during the span of time between the painting of the frescoes in the Peruzzi chapel (c. 1310-1315) and those in the Bardi chapel (c. 1325-1330) in the Florentine Basilica of Santa Croce.

11

MASTER OF THE ST. CECILIA
*Enthroned Madonna
and Child*

Exhibited from 1902 to 1998 in the Museo Civico of Pescia, this painting is a work fundamental for the history of Fourteenth century Florentine painting. It is attributed to an anonymous contemporary and collaborator of Giotto, whose hand is recognisable also in some parts of the frescoes with *Scenes from the life of St. Francis* in the upper Basilica of Assisi.

Giottesque Room

The works

1. BERNARDO DADDI
(above)
*Enthroned Madonna with Child
between two Angels, St. John
the Baptist and St. Luke*
1333
Tempera on wood
219×132 cm
Inv. 1890 no. 6170

2. JACOPO DEL CASENTINO
*St. Bartholomew enthroned
with eight Angels; Two Prophets
and Christ bestowing Blessings*
(trilobes)
1340-1345
Tempera on wood; 266×122 cm
Inv. 1890 no. 440

3. JACOPO DEL CASENTINO
*St. John the Baptist
St. Egidius
St. John the Evangelist*
In the cuspids: *Three Prophets*
1330-1335
Tempera on wood
117,5×43; 118×43; 116,2×42,5 cm
Inv. 1890 nos. 8571, 8572, 8573
Restored: 1998

**4. MASTER OF THE
DOMINICAN EFFIGIES**
*Madonna with Child and Saints;
Coronation of the Virgin and Saints*
1340-1345
Tempera on wood
52,5×180 et 52,7×180 cm
Inv. 1890 nos. 4633 and 4634

5. PUCCIO DI SIMONE
*Virgin of Humility;
St. Lawrence; St. Onofrio;
St. James Major;
St. Bartholomew*
1350-1360
Tempera on wood
132×190 cm
Inv. 1890 no. 8569

6. BERNARDO DADDI
Crucifixion
In the back: *St. Christopher*
1330-1335
Tempera on wood
41×18 cm
Inv. 1890 no. 8563

7. BERNARDO DADDI
St. Bartholomew (left)
St. Lawrence (right)
1340-1345
Tempera on wood
111,5×40,5 et 110,5×40 cm
Inv. 1890 nos. 8706, 8707

8. BERNARDO DADDI
*Crucifixion with Mourners
and Mary Magdalene
at the Foot of the Cross*
1343
Tempera on wood; 126×60,5 cm
Inv. 1890 no. 8570

9. BERNARDO DADDI
*Coronation of the Virgin
with Angels and Saints*
1340-1345
Tempera on wood
188,5×270 cm
Inv. 1890 no. 3449
Restored: 1999

10. BERNARDO DADDI
*Painted Crucifix:
The grieving Virgin
and St. John
and Stories
of Christ's Passion*
1340-1345
Tempera on wood
350×275 cm
Inv. 1890 no. 442

11. BERNARDO DADDI
*Crucifixion
among the Mourners
and Mary Magdalene*
In the side panels:
PUCCIO DI SIMONE
*St. Mary Magdalene,
St. Michael Archangel,
St. Julian, St. Martha*
1340-1345
Tempera on wood
104×47 cm (central panel))
79,5×31,5 cm (each side panel)
Inv. 1890 nos. 443 and 6140
Restored: 1995

12. BERNARDO DADDI
*Enthroned Madonna
with Child and Saints;
Crucifixion
among the Mourners;
Legend of the three Live Men
and three Dead Men*
c. 1340
Tempera on wood
55×47,5 cm
Inv. 1890 nos. 8567, 8566; 6152, 6153

13. TADDEO GADDI
*Scenes from the Life of Christ:
Ascension, Annunciation*
(two lunettes);
*Visitation,
Adoration of the Shepherds,
Adoration of the Magi,
Presentation of Jesus
at the Temple,
Disputation with the Doctors,
Baptism of Jesus,
Transfiguration,
The Last Supper, Crucifixion,
Resurrection of Christ,
Apparition of the Marys,
Incredulity of St. Thomas*
(12 panels);
*Scenes from the Life
of St. Francis of Assisi:
St. Francis renounces
worldly goods,
The Crèche of Greccio,
The dream of Innocent III,
Approval of the Rule,*

*Preaching before Honorius III,
St. Francis on the fiery chariot,
St. Francis receiving the stigmata,
The martyrdom
of the Franciscans at Ceuta,
Apparition at the Capitol of Arles,
Funeral of St. Francis
and incredulity of Jerome*
(10panels)
c. 1335-1340
Tempera on wood
72×158×6,2 cm (total lunettes)
40,5×36,5; 41×29,5; 41,5×30;
41×31 cm (panels)
Inv. 1890 nos. 8581-8593
and nos. 8594-8603

14. TADDEO GADDI
*Madonna with Child
St. John the Baptist
and St. Peter*
In the cuspids:
Announcing Angel (left)
*Our Lady of the
Annunciation*
(right)
1345-1350
Tempera on wood
48,5×15,7 and 48×16 cm (each)
Inv. 1890 no. 3144

15. TADDEO GADDI
Madonna with Child
c. 1355
In the lunette:
NICCOLÒ DI PIETRO GERINI
*Benediction of Christ
between two Prophets*
In the predella:
NICCOLÒ DI PIETRO GERINI
*Christ as the Man
of Sorrows
among Mourners
and six Saints*
c. 1395-1400
Tempera on wood
184×129 cm
Inv. 1890 no. 448

16. TADDEO GADDI
*Enthroned Madonna
and Child among
Saints and Angels*
c. 1325-1330
Tempera on wood
52,5×26,5 cm
Deposits Inv. no. 169

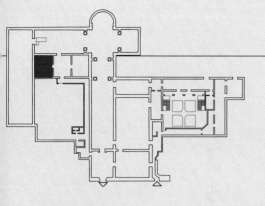

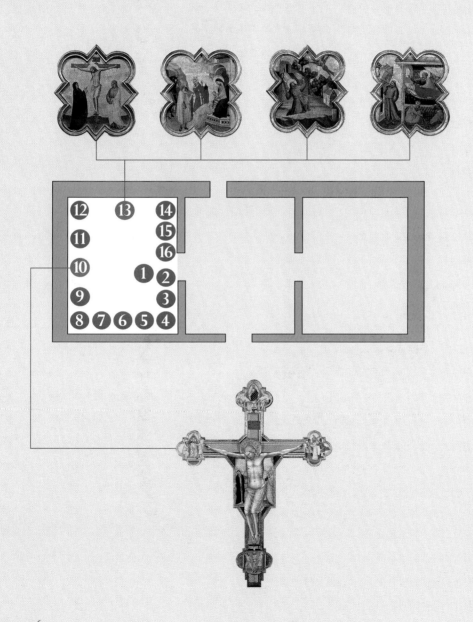

BERNARDO DADDI
Painted Crucifix: The grieving Virgin and St. John and Stories of Christ's Passion

This large, shaped *Crucifix* possibly comes from the Florentine Church of San Donato in Polverosa and was presumably placed above the high altar, hanging from the ceiling.
In medieval churches this type of image was often placed on top of the iconostasis, i.e. the dividing wall between the presbytery and the choir, as is clearly shown in the Greccio nativity scene painted by Giotto in the Basilica of St. Francis in Assisi.

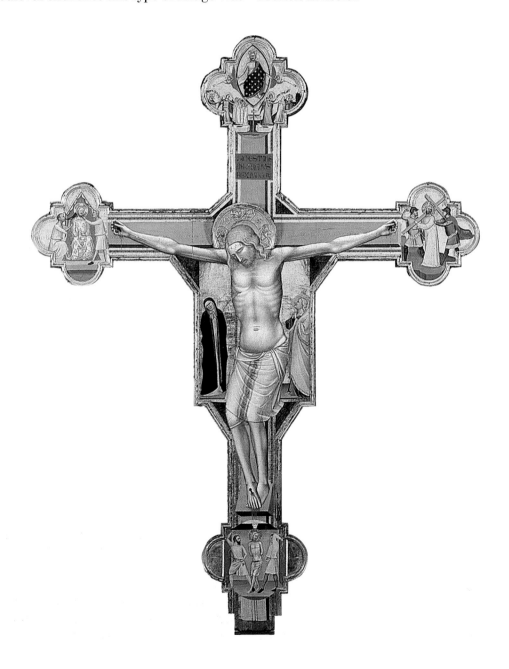

13

TADDEO GADDI
Scenes from the Life of Christ and of St. Francis of Assisi

These panels came from the sacristy of the Basilica of Santa Croce where they decorated wooden furniture, perhaps a reliquary cupboard. The single episodes from the life of St. Francis are illustrated in a parallel with the Life of Christ: for example, the episode with the *Imposition of the stigmata to St. Francis* corresponds to the *Crucifixion*. Giotto's most direct pupil, Taddeo was the first to include his master's innovations: note the solid volumetric disposition of the figures and the well-constructed architectural perspective, which indicate a *modus operandi* very far removed from the transcendent and ethereal world of Byzantine painting.

99

Room of the Orcagnas and their followers

The works

**1. ANDREA DI CIONE
KNOWN AS ORCAGNA**
*Enthroned Madonna
with Child and Saints*
1353-1355
Tempera on wood; 127×224 cm
Inv. 1890 no. 3469

**2. ANDREA DI CIONE
KNOWN AS ORCAGNA**
Pentecost
1365-1370
Tempera on wood; 195×273,6 cm
Deposits Inv. no. 165

3. NARDO DI CIONE
*Thronum Gratiae;
St. Romualdus;
St. John Evangelist*
In the predella:
*Scenes from the life
of St. Romualdus*
1365
Tempera on wood
295×216 cm
Inv 1890 no. 8464
Restored: 2000

**4. MASTER OF THE ASHMOLEAN
MUSEUM PREDELLA**
*St. Lawrence
St. Vescovus*
1360-1365
Tempera on wood
84×31,8 et 87×31,5 cm
Inv. 1890 nos. 8702 and 8701

**5. MASTER OF THE
ST. NICCOLÒ ALTAR**
*Virgin of Humility
and four Angels*
1360-1365
Tempera on wood
105,5×61,5 cm
Inv. 1890 no. 4698

6. NICCOLÒ DI TOMMASO
*Coronation of the Virgin
with eighteen Saints
and deux Angels*
c. 1365-1370
Tempera on wood
90×43 cm
Inv. 1890 no. 8580

7. JACOPO DI CIONE
*Crucifixion between four Angels
and Mourners at the foot of the Cross*
c. 1370
Tempera on wood
275,5×152 cm
Inv. 1890 no. 4670

8. JACOPO DI CIONE
*Virgin with Child
and two kneeling donors*
In the cuspids:
Annunciation
1360-1365 cm
Tempera on wood; 59×63 cm
Inv. 1890 no. 8465

9. JACOPO DI CIONE
Virgin of Humility
1365-1370
Tempera on wood
104,7×66 cm
Inv. Deposits no. 132

**10. WORKSHOP OF
JACOPO DI CIONE**
*Massacre of the Innocents;
Adoration of the Magi;
Flight into Egypt*
1375-1385
Tempera on wood
149,5×109 cm
Inv. 1890 no. 5887
Restored: 1991

11. MATTEO DI PACINO
*Vision of St. Bernard;
Christ bestowing Blessings*
In the cuspids:
Annunciation
In the predella:
*Scenes from the life
of St. Bernard, St. Benedict,
St. John evangelist,
St. Quintinus
and St. Galgano*
c. 1365
Tempera on wood
173×199 cm
Inv. 1890 no. 8463

12. MATTEO DI PACINO
*Charity
of St. Anthony abbot*
1370-1375
Tempera on wood
53,5×49,5 cm
Inv. 1890 no. 460

**13. MASTER OF THE
RINUCCINI CHAPEL**
*St. Michael Archangel,
St. Bartholomew,
St. Julian and the donor*
After 1348
Tempera on wood
158×86 cm
Inv. 1890 no. 6134

**14. JACOPO DI CIONE,
NICCOLÒ DI TOMMASO,
SIMONE DI LAPO**
*Coronation of the Virgin
and Saints*
1372-1373
Tempera on wood
350×190 cm
Inv. 1890 no. 456

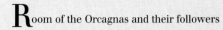

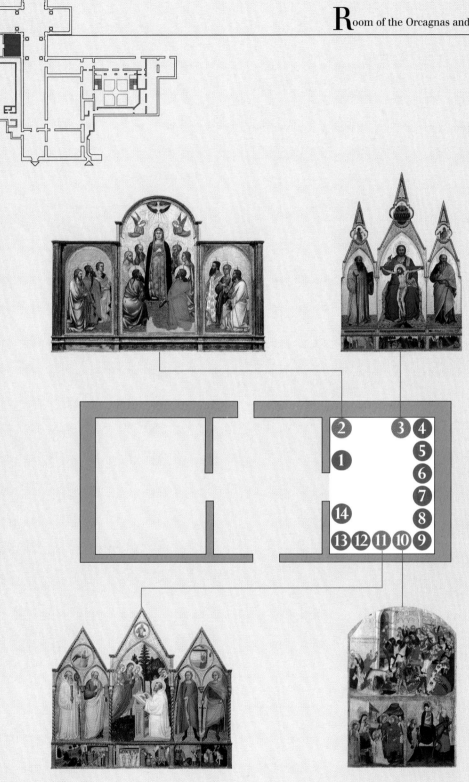

2

ANDREA ORCAGNA
Pentecost

This triptych (c. 1365-1370) reveals the characteristics of Andrea Orcagna's painting style in the last phase of his life; with its square spaces, the rigid frontal arrangement of the figures and the limited chromatic range, it must have fitted harmoniously in the Romanesque Church of the Santi Apostoli in Florence, where it came from. In the second half of the Eighteenth century it was transferred to the Church of Badia, from where it was passed to the Accademia Gallery in 1939. It is likely that Andrea's younger brother Jacopo assisted in the painting work, and his hand can be seen in areas of softer, more blended application of colour in some of the Apostles, and hints of softness in the volumetric construction.

NARDO DI CIONE
Thronum Gratiae

This polyptych was commissioned by Giovanni Ghiberti for his chapel in the Chapter of Santa Maria degli Angioli. It was removed and taken (c. 1750) to the Della Stufa Chapel, dedicated to St. Andrew, and on this occasion St. John Evangelist was repainted to resemble St. Andrew. Today the triptych has resumed its original appearance.

10

WORKSHOP OF JACOPO DI CIONE
Massacre of the Innocents;
Adoration of the Magi; Flight into Egypt

This panel was in the past attributed to an anonymous master known as the Master of Christ's Childhood because of the scenes depicted here, but has now been included in the early works of Jacopo di Cione, brother of Andrea Orcagna and quite close in his lively narrative style to Niccolò di Tommaso.

11

MATTEO DI PACINO
Vision of St. Bernard;
St. Benedict and St. John Evangelist

The panel, attributed in the past to an anony-mous Master of the Rinuccini Chapel, is now rec-ognized as the work of Matteo di Pacino, a painter trained in the Orcagna shop and thus possess-ing a style marked by a strong sense of volumetric disposition and monumentality, who worked with Giovanni da Milano on the fresco decora-tions of the Rinuccini Chapel in Santa Croce, completing them when da Milano left Florence. Due to his contact with Giovanni da Milano, the painter's chromatic range is warmer and brighter than that of Orcagna's closest followers.

Giovanni da Milano Room

These recently restored and rearranged rooms bring together the varied and exhaustive range of late Gothic Florentine painting. These include portable altarpieces and grand polyptychs, as well as a collection of nine works by Lorenzo Monaco an incomparably beautiful group of exceptional rarity, through which we can become familiar with the work of this great Gothic painter in all the phases of his artistic career.

The works

1. FLORENTINE PAINTER (and MARIOTTO DI NARDO)
Annunciation
In the predella:
Adoration of the Shepherds,
Adoration of the Magi,
Presentation at the Temple
On the coping:
The Prophets Isaiah and Daniel
Second half XIV century
Tempera on wood; 280×110 cm
Inv. 1890 nos. 455 and 6098

2. DON SILVESTRO DE' GHERARDUCCI
Madonna of Humility
and Angels
c. 1370-1375
Tempera on wood; 164×80 cm
Inv. 1890 no. 3161

3. MASTER OF THE ASHMOLEAN MUSEUM PREDELLA
Madonna and Child
1365
Tempera on wood; diameter 116 cm
Deposits Inv. no. 178
Restored: 2000

4. ANDREA DI BONAIUTO
St. Agnes
St. Domitilla
1365-1370
Tempera on wood; 66×28 cm (each)
Inv. 189 no. 3145

5. GIOVANNI DA MILANO
Christ in Pietà, Lamentation
of the Virgin Mary,
St. Mary Magdalene
and St. John the Evangelist
1365
Tempera on wood; 121×63 cm
Inv. 1890 no. 8467. Restored: 2001

6. MASTER OF THE ACCADEMIA MISERICORDIA (GIOVANNI GADDI?)
Virgin of Mercy
c. 1380
Tempera on wood; 64×35 cm
Inv. 1890 no. 8562

7. MASTER OF THE ACCADEMIA MISERICORDIA (GIOVANNI GADDI?)
Stigmata of St. Francis; Nativity;
Conversion of St. Paul
c. 1375
Tempera on wood; 50×94 cm
Inv. 1890 no. 8565

8. MASTER OF THE ACCADEMIA MISERICORDIA (GIOVANNI GADDI?)
Madonna and Child
between St. Peter
and St. Paul
c. 1355-1360
Tempera on wood
146×63 cm
Inv. 1890 no. 437

9. GIOTTO DI STEFANO KNOWN AS GIOTTINO (ATTR. TO)
Madonna and Child enthroned
between two Saints
and eight Angels
c. 1356
Tempera on wood
310×152 cm
Without Inv.

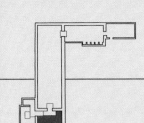

2

Don Silvestro de' Gherarducci
Madonna of Humility and Angels

Silvestro de' Gherarducci entered the Monastery of Santa Maria degli Angioli in 1348 aged nine. He worked with Lorenzo Monaco as a painter and illuminator, never losing the characteristic rich and colourful decorative elements which denote his Sienese origins. The *Virgin of Humility* (c. 1370-1375), which depicts the Virgin sitting on the ground on a cushion, is a subject particularly dear to late Gothic tastes.

4

ANDREA DI BONAIUTO
St. Agnes
St. Domitilla

Andrea di Bonaiuto (also known as Andrea da Firenze), a Florentine painter who trained in the studio of Nardo di Cione, brother of Andrea Orcagna, is famous above all for having frescoed the Spagnuoli Chapel in the Santa Maria Novel-la Monastery. This small diptych (c. 1365-1370) is stylistically and therefore chronologically close to that work and demonstrates the painter's knowledge and assimilation of the work of Giovanni da Milano, who was present and working in Florence in those very years. The two female figures shown here particularly stand out for the courtly sophistication of their costly clothes and the intense use of "chiaroscuro".

5

GIOVANNI DA MILANO
Christ in Pietà

This small devotional panel represents one of the greatest achievements of Fourteenth century painting in Florence after the death of Giotto. It was painted for the Florentine Church of San Girolamo alla Costa, dated 1365 and signed, and at the bottom bears the coats of arms of the Strozzi and Rinieri families who obviously commissioned it. Giovanni da Milano's painting, with its intense sensitivity to colour and moving sentimentality offers an alternative to the severe style of Orcagna, which had dominated the gloomy period following the Great Plague of 1348. With Giovanni's work, Florence opened up to the new insistence of the International Gothic trend.

6

MASTER OF THE ACCADEMIA MISERICORDIA (GIOVANNI GADDI?)

Virgin of Mercy

This panel comes from the Augustinian Monastery of Santa Maria in Candeli. It portrays the *Virgin as Mater Misericordiae*, sheltering under her mantle, held up by two angels, twenty-three Augustinian nuns and four women, probably the donors of the tabernacle.

Once considered the work of an anonymous Fifteenth century painter, it is now attributed to a master who takes his name from this painting, to whom several other works in the same room have also been attributed. The calligraphic elegance and delicate treatment of color seem to indicate that the painter may have worked in illumination as well. It has recently been hypothesized that the Master of the Accademia Misericordia may be Giovanni Gaddi, the elder brother of the more famous Agnolo Gaddi, documented as a painter from 1369-1386.

Late Fourteenth Century Room

The works

1. GIOVANNI DEL BIONDO
Presentation at the Temple among St. John the Baptist and St. Benedict
In the cuspids: *Christ bestowing Blessings between two Seraphim*
In the predella: *Announcement to Zaccharia; Birth of the Baptist Herod's banquet*
1364; Tempera on wood; 215×200 cm
Inv. 1890 no. 8462

2. GIOVANNI DEL BIONDO
Enthroned St. John the Evangelist
In the cuspid:
Christ bestowing Blessings
In the predella:
Ascension of St. John Evangelist
c. 1380-1385
Tempera on wood; 335×113 cm
Inv. 1890 nos. 444, 446

3. CENNI DI FRANCESCO
Virgin and Child among eight Saints and four Angels
In the predella:
Christ as the Man of Sorrows among the mourners
Late XIV century; Tempera on wood; 88×49 cm. Inv. 1890 no. 6119

4. GIOVANNI DEL BIONDO
Annunciation
In the cuspids: *Christ at the Column, Crucifixion* and *Resurrection*
In the predella:
Christ as the Man of Sorrows between mourners and Saints
1380-1385
Tempera on wood; 404×381 cm
Inv. 1890 no. 8606

5. "FRANCESCO"
Madonna and Child between two Angels and two Saints
In the cuspid: *Benediction of Christ*
In the predella: *Christ teaching*
1391; Tempera on wood; 213×103 cm
Inv. 1890 no. 6154

6. SPINELLO ARETINO
Enthroned Madonna with Child and four Angels; The Saints Paolino, St. John the Baptist, St. Andrew and St. Matthew Evangelist
1391; Tempera on wood; 170×209 cm
Inv. 1890 no. 8461

7. LORENZO DI NICCOLÒ
Coronation of the Virgin with four musical Angels; St. Bartholomew and *St. Zanobius*
c. 1400-1410
Tempera on wood; 156×174 cm
Inv. 1890 nos. 6087, 6088, 4656
Restored: 1995 (both compartments

8. MARIOTTO DI NARDO
Madonna with Child and Saints
In the cuspids: *Announcing Angel, Our Lady of the Annunciation, Crucifixion*
In the predella:
Histoires de la vie de la Vierge
c. 1390-1395
Tempera on wood; 319×267 cm
Inv. 1890 nos. 8612; 3260, 3259, 3258; 8613

9. CENNI DI FRANCESCO (above)
Nativity
c. 1395-1400
Tempera on wood; 80×147 cm
Inv. 1890 no. 6139

10. MARIOTTO DI NARDO (below)
Crucifixion and four Stories of Life of St. Nicolas
c. 1410-1415
Tempera on wood; 40×242 cm
Inv. 1890 no. 9206. Restored: 1985

11. NICCOLÒ DI PIETRO GERINI
Madonna with Child and Saints
Beginning XV century
Tempera on wood; 136,5×64,5 cm
Inv. 1890 no. 8578

12. NICCOLÒ DI PIETRO GERINI
Christ as the Man of Sorrows with the symbols of Passion
In the cuspid:
The Redeemer and four Saints
In the predella:
The funeral of a brother in the Compagnia del Pellegrino
1404-1408
Tempera on wood; 351×158 cm
Inv. 1890 nos. 5048, 5067, 5066
Restored: 2004

13. SPINELLO ARETINO
St. Stephen
In the cuspid: *Crucifixion with mourners*
c. 1400-1405
Tempera on wood; 93×33 cm
Inv. 1890 no. 6287

14. MASTER OF BORGO ALLA COLLINA
Crucifixion among the Virgin, St. Francis and kneeling donor
First half of XV century
Tempera on wood; 70×51,5 cm
Inv. 1890 no. 3149

15. GIOVANNI DAL PONTE
St. Helen
and *St. James the Elder*
1420-1430
Tempera on wood; 94×39,5 (each)
Inv. 1890 nos. 8746, 8744

16. GIOVANNI DAL PONTE
Coronation of the Virgin with four musical Angels and St. Francis, St. John the Baptist, St. Ivo and St. Dominic
In the cuspids:
Descent into Limbo; Annunciation
c. 1420-1430
Tempera on wood; 208×215,5 cm
Inv. 1890 no. 458

17. GIOVANNI DAL PONTE
St. Julian; St. John the Baptist
c. 1430
Tempera on wood; 59×26 cm (each)
Inv. 1890 nos. 6232, 6105

18. ROSSELLO DI JACOPO FRANCHI
St. Francis; St. John the Baptist
c. 1400-1410
Tempera on wood; 135×68,5 cm (each)
Inv. 1890 nos. 6094, 6103

19. ROSSELLO DI JACOPO FRANCHI
Coronation of the Virgin with Angels and Saints
In the cuspids:
Benediction of the Eternal, Two Prophets and *Annunciation*
On pilaster at the left: Saints: *Saints*
In the predella: *Christ as the Man of Sorrows among mourners and Saints*
1420
Tempera on wood; 344×394 cm
Inv. 1890 no. 8460

20. BICCI DI LORENZO
St. Andrew and St. Michael St. Jerome and St. Lawrence
c. 1435
Tempera on wood
175×58,5 cm (each)
Deposits Inv. no. 12

21. BICCI DI LORENZO
St. Paul, St. Philip (?) and St. Bartholomew; St. Andrew, St. James, St. Apostle
c. 1420
Tempera on wood; 55×19,5 cm (each)
Inv. 1890 nos. 6141, 6143, 6141; 6142, 6142, 6143

22. FLORENTINE PAINTER
Virgin of Humility between two Angels
c. 1390-1399
Tempera on wood; 102×54 cm
Inv. 1890 no. 465

23. JACOPO CAMBI
Coronation of the Virgin between eight Angels and fourteen Saints
In the upper border:
Eleven scenes from the life of the Virgin delimited by two Prophets and ten Saints
1336
Embroidered altar-facing; 106×440 cm
18 cm upper border
Ancient fabrics Inv. 1913 no. 881

24. NICCOLÒ DI PIETRO GERINI
Enthroned Madonna and Child with two Saints
c. 1400-1410
Tempera on wood; 301×128,5 cm;
Inv. 1890 no. 439

25. BICCI DI LORENZO
St. Paul; St. Benedict; St. Giovanni Gualberto; St. Peter
c. 1430-1435
Tempera on wood 54×19 cm (each)
Inv. 1890 nos. 5985, 5986, 5987, 5988

26. LIPPO D'ANDREA
Enthroned Madonna and Child with Saints
In the cuspids: *Two Saints*
In the predella: *Nativity* and *Scenes from the lives of Saints Catherine and Francis* (left), *Zanobius and Marie Magdalene* (right)
First half of XV century
Tempera on wood; 229×287 cm
Deposits Inv. no. 18

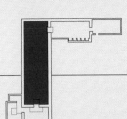

27. NICCOLÒ DI PIETRO GERINI
Enthroned Madonna and Child among St. Anthony abbot, St. John, St. Lawrence and St. Julian
1404
Tempera on wood; 183×285,9 cm
Inv. 1890 no. 8610

28. MARIOTTO DI NARDO
Annunciation
c. 1400-1410
Tempera on wood; 165,5×155 cm
Inv. 1890 no. 463

29. MARIOTTO DI NARDO
Madonna with Child and Saints (Philip and John the Baptist)
In the cuspid: *Two Angels*
c. 1418
Tempera on wood; 244×126 cm
Inv. 1890 no. 473

30. SPINELLO ARETINO, NICCOLÒ DI PIETRO GERINI, LORENZO DI NICCOLÒ
Coronation of the Virgin, Angels and Saints
1401
Tempera on wood; 280×279 cm
Inv. 1890 no. 8468

31. NICCOLÒ DI PIETRO GERINI
Crucifixion with St. Francis in adoration and Saints
In the cuspids: *Annunciation; Christ bestowing blessings*
c. 1400
Tempera on wood; 114×210 cm
Inv. 1890 no. 3152
In the cuspids:
AGNOLO DI DOMENICO DEL MAZZIERE
The four Evangelists
Early XVI century
Tempera on wood; 84×210 cm
Inv. 1890 no. 5061

32. MARIOTTO DI NARDO
Madonna with Child and Saints
c. 1380-1400
Tempera on wood; 192×132 cm
Inv. 1890 no. 3460

33. LORENZO DI BICCI
St. Julian and St. Zanobius
c. 1380-1400
Tempera on wood; 131×82,5 cm
Inv. 1890 no. 5410

34. NICCOLÒ DI PIETRO GERINI
The Holy Trinity with St. Francis and St. Mary Magdalene
c. 1380-1385
Tempera on wood; 86×61 cm
Inv. 1890 no. 3944

35. LORENZO DI BICCI
Enthroned St. Martin
In the predella:
Charity of St. Martin
c. 1380-1385
Tempera on wood
203×99 cm; 64,5×99 cm (predella)
Deposits Inv. no. 174
Inv. 1890 no. 462 (predella)

4

GIOVANNI DEL BIONDO
Annunciation

This large and complex polyptych was situated on the altar of the Cavalcanti Chapel in Santa Maria Novella. It came to us in excellent condition, complete with almost all its accessorie, and constitutes an example of the high technical quality of the work of 14th century Florentine studios.

6

SPINELLO ARETINO
Enthroned Madonna with Child and four Angels; St. Paul, St. John the Baptist, St. Andrew and St. Matthew Evangelist

This altarpiece, which comes from the Church of Sant'Andrea a Lucca, is signed and dated 1391 on the step in the central panel. Spinello Aretino was first trained in the vigorous artistic atmosphere of Arezzo but later worked all over Tuscany – in addition to Arezzo and Lucca, Florence, where he worked for the Opera del Duomo in 1387; Pisa, where he frescoed the *Stories of Saints Efisio and Potito* in the Camposanto; Siena, where he worked in the Cathedral in 1405 and in the Sala di Balìa in Palazzo Pubblico in 1408. The Accademia Gallery possesses another work commissioned of Spinello, Niccolò Gerini and Lorenzo di Niccolò in 1399: the polyptych of the *Coronation of the Virgin and Saints* painted for the high altar of the Church of Santa Felicita in Florence (Inv. 1890 no. 8468). On a basic scheme that is still Giottesque, Spinello grafts episodes and details imbued with Gothic elegance in a style distinguished for its lively narration and vivid sense of decoration.

8

MARIOTTO DI NARDO
Madonna Child and Saints

This polyptych (c. 1390-1395), commissioned by the Corsini family for Church of St. Gaggio, records the mature phase of Mariotto di Nardo's work. It was an active artist in Florence between the Fourteenth and Fifteenth centuries, also for commissions of a certain importance. His success was probably due to the Orcagnesque elements in his style, the excessive hardness of which was diluted with warmer colouring and more charming decorative elements. The work by Mariotto reached us complete with all its elements, i.e. the predella showing *Scenes from the Life of the Virgin* and the large cuspidate panels with *Annunciation* and *Crucifixion*, and thus provides us with an idea of how ornate the altars of the most important Medieval churches must have been.

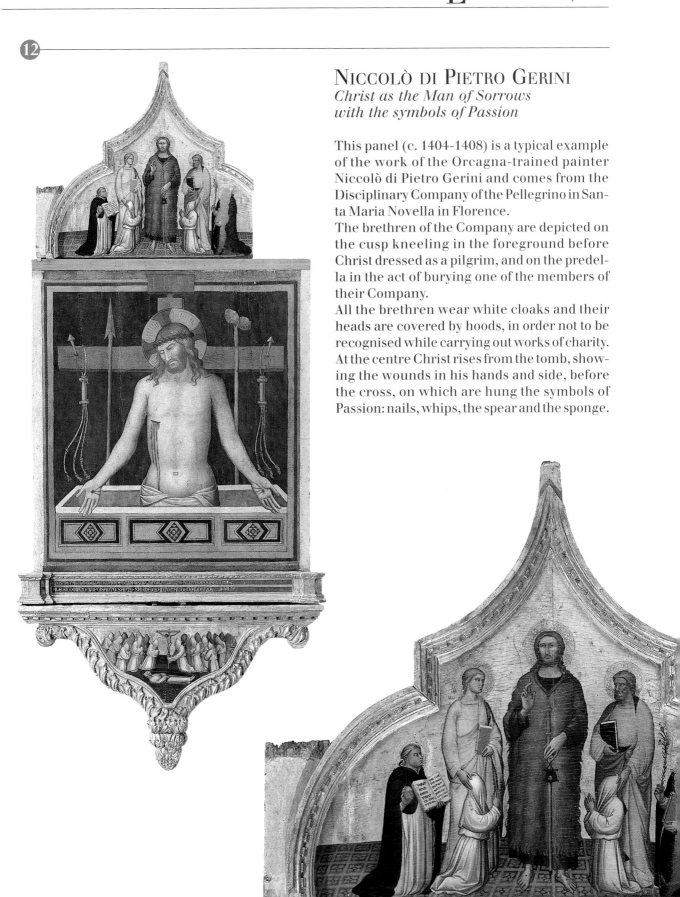

Niccolò di Pietro Gerini
Christ as the Man of Sorrows
with the symbols of Passion

This panel (c. 1404-1408) is a typical example of the work of the Orcagna-trained painter Niccolò di Pietro Gerini and comes from the Disciplinary Company of the Pellegrino in Santa Maria Novella in Florence.
The brethren of the Company are depicted on the cusp kneeling in the foreground before Christ dressed as a pilgrim, and on the predella in the act of burying one of the members of their Company.
All the brethren wear white cloaks and their heads are covered by hoods, in order not to be recognised while carrying out works of charity. At the centre Christ rises from the tomb, showing the wounds in his hands and side, before the cross, on which are hung the symbols of Passion: nails, whips, the spear and the sponge.

13

SPINELLO ARETINO
St. Stephen

The saint is depicted holding in his right hand
the banner of the Wool Guild, which was quite
a powerful corporation in Florence and the
same motif is repeated on the sides of the predella. This little tabernacle (c. 1400-1405)
demonstrates the preciosity of Spinello's later style, and to a greater extent, the small *Crucifixion* in the cusp panel, where the drapery
of the crouching figures flows with inimitable
elegance.

16

GIOVANNI DAL PONTE
Coronation of the Virgin
with four musical Angels and St. Francis,
St. John the Baptist, St. Ivo and St. Dominic

Giovanni di Marco, known as Giovanni dal Ponte, received his nickname from the fact that he came from the florentine Parish of Santo Stefano al Ponte. He was an artist of great skill, clearly able to assimilate into his original artistic language the cultural influences emanating from the broad panorama of Florentine art in the early Fifteenth century. The artist was first attracted by Spinello Aretino, then by the Gothic International style introduced to Florence in those years by Lorenzo Monaco and Gherardo Starnina. In the third decade of the century (c. 1420-1430), to which this polyptych is dated, he freely adopted the Renaissance innovations introduced by Masolino, Beato Angelico and Masaccio, conferring greater composure on the figures but without abandoning his propensity to impetuous rhythms in the drawing as well as in the drapery of the figures.

19

ROSSELLO DI JACOPO FRANCHI
*Coronation of the Virgin
with Angels and Saints*

This grand and highly decorated polyptych
(1420) is the work of Rossello di Jacopo Franchi,
an artist who trained in the late Gothic period
and continued to paint his sweet and rather
mannered figures until the end of his life (1456),
long after the advent in Florence of Masaccio
and the rise of the early Renaissance.

23

JACOPO CAMBI
*Coronation of the Virgin between
eight Angels and fourteen Saints*

This beautiful example of embroidery in *opus
florentinum*, one of the most magnificent to
come down to us, decorated the high altar of
the Church of Santa Maria Novella in Florence.
It was probably commissioned by Fra Jacopo
of Andrea Aldobrandini, who was given other
commissions for furnishings for the Dominican Monastery. The main scene with the *Coronation of the Virgin* is flanked by seven figures
on each side, delimited to the right by the pa-
triarch Abraham and to the left by king David.
On the upper border are eleven stories from

the life of Maria. In the lower center are the
signature and the date: "IACOBUS CAMBI DE FLO-
RENTIA ME FECIT MCCCXXXVI". Decorations of this
type were highly appreciated and widely dif-
fused in the Fourteenth century, especially in
France and Spain, where another altar-facing
embroidered by Geri di Lapo is still to be found
in the Cathedral of Manresa in Catalonia. As
compared to the latter, Jacopo Cambi's work
is more elegant in the variety and fantasy of
the stitches and in the Gothic style of the drawing. For the "ornate" naturalism of the figures
and for some of the facial types (St. Peter and
St. Paul), the most authoritative critics have
linked this work to the refined culture of the
Master of Figline.

Lorenzo Monaco Room

The works

1. AGNOLO GADDI
*Virgin of Humility
with six Angels*
c. 1390-1396
Tempera on wood
118×62 cm
Inv. 1890 no. 461

2. ANONYMOUS FLORENTINE
*Coronation of the Virgin
with Saints*
In the cuspid:
Benediction of the Eternal Father
c. 1390-1399
Tempera on wood
111×53 cm
Inv. 1890 no. 8579

3. LORENZO MONACO
Oration in the Garden
c. 1395-1400
Tempera on wood
223×117 cm
Inv. 1890 no. 438

4. LORENZO MONACO
*Christ as the Man of Sorrows
with the symbols of Passion*
1404
Tempera on wood
265×172 cm
Inv. 1890 no. 467

5. LORENZO MONACO
Madone and Child with Saints
1408
Tempera on wood; 120×65 cm
Inv. 1890 no. 470

6. LORENZO MONACO
*Enthroned Madonna with Child
and Saints (St. Bartholomew,
St. John the Baptist, St. Thaddeus
and St. Benedict)*
In the cuspids: *Announcing Angel,
Le Benediction of Christ*
and *Our Lady of the Annunciation*
In the lateral pinnacles:
Two Prophets
1410
Tempera on wood; 274×261 cm
Inv. 1890 no. 468

7. LORENZO MONACO
*Christ Crucified and Angels;
Sorrowing Virgin; St. John the
Evangelist*
c. 1400-1413
Tempera on wood
78×65 cm; 74×18 cm; 78×65
Inv. 1890 nos. 2141, 2169, 2140
Restored: 2004

8. LORENZO MONACO
The Redeemer bestowing blessings
c. 1415
Tempera on wood; 82×41 cm
Inv. 1890 no. 10102

9. LORENZO MONACO
*Annunciation among St.Catherine
of Alexandria, St. Anthony,
St. Proculous and St. Francis of Assisi*
c. 1418
Tempera on wood; 206×231,5 cm
Inv. 1890 no. 8458

10. LORENZO MONACO
Painted Cross
c. 1400-1410
Tempera on wood; 220×190 cm
Inv. 1890 no. 3153

11. BARTOLOMEO DI FRUOSINO
Painted and shaped Cross
1411
Tempera on wood; 280×190 cm
Inv. 1890 no. 3147. Restored: 1986

12. *88 Icons of Russian, gréco-
byzantine and dalmate School*
XVII-XVIII centuries
Tempera/oil on wood

13. LORENZO MONACO
*The Madonna "del latte"
with Saints and Angels*
In the door at left:
**MASTER
OF THE SHERMAN PREDELLA**
*Announcing Angel;
Crucifixion with mourners
and St. Mary Magdalene*
In the door at left:
Our Lady of the Annunciation

*and Saints
(Paul, Gregory Pope and Dominic)*
1390, 1425-1430
Tempera on wood; 148×140 cm
Inv. 1890 no. 3227

14. LORENZO MONACO
*Enthroned Madonna and Child
among Sts. John the Baptist,
Lucia, Anthony Abbot, Peter,
Julian and Catherine of Alexandria*
c. 1395-1400
Tempera on wood; 114×69 cm
Inv. 1890 no. 3234

15. LORENZO MONACO
*St. Moses; St. John the Baptist;
St. Peter; St. Paul*
c. 1395-1400
Tempera on wood
100×40 cm (each)
Inv. 1890 nos. 8704, 8705, 8708, 8709

16. LORENZO MONACO
*St. Catherine of Alexandria
St. Caius Pope*
In the cuspid: *Announcing Angel;
Our Lady of the Annunciation*
1390-1395
Tempera on wood
226×72; 218×51 cm
Inv. 1890 nos. 8605, 8604

**17. MASTER OF SANTA VERDIANA
(TOMMASO DEL MAZZA)**
*Virgin of Humility
with four Angels and Saints*
c. 1370-1400
Tempera on wood
87×52 cm
Inv. 1890 no. 3156

18. AGNOLO GADDI
*Madonna "del latte"
and Saints (Catherine
of Alexandria and John
the Baptist; Mary Magdalene
and Anthony Abbot)*
c. 1380
Tempera on wood
140×65 cm
Inv. 1890 no. 8577

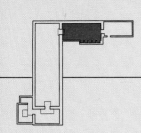

THE COLLECTION OF RUSSIAN ICONS

The Collection of Russian Icons, put together by the Grand Dukes of Lorraine, is displayed in the niches of the right-hand wall. The quality of these pieces is rather discontinuous and only rarely of exceptional calibre; therefore it might be said that the group as a whole is more significant for research and knowledge of the Lorraine passion for collecting rather than for the history of Russian art.

3

LORENZO MONACO
Oration in the Garden

This is one of the oldest panels by Lorenzo Monaco and was painted (c. 1395-1400) for the Florentine Monastery of Santa Maria degli Angioli, where the artist lived. His deep knowledge of Giotto's painting, who must have been directly known to him, is evident from the style, learned in the Orcagna studio. However, at the same time the fluid and extended flowing of the drapery places his work within the modern taste for International Gothicism.

6

LORENZO MONACO
*Enthroned Madonna
with Child and Saints*

This polyptych (1410) formerly decorated the Church of San Bartolomeo in Montoliveto near Florence and confirms Lorenzo Monaco's ability with chromatic and decorative effects, even in works of larger dimensions.

Having now fully mastered his expressive medium, the great master emphasises here the outlines of the figures with impeccable fluidity and harmony while the chromatic range seems infused with the purest light.

It must be remembered that Lorenzo Monaco was also an illuminator and his pen decorated with gold and bright colours many of the manuscripts made in the Monastery of Santa Maria degli Angioli in Florence, where he lived as a Camaldolensian monk.

SCA·CATHARINA·   SCS·ANTONIUS·   AVE·GRATIA·PLENA·   ECCE·ANCILLA·DOMINI   SCS·PROCULUS·   SCS·FRANCISC·

9

LORENZO MONACO
Annunciation and Saints

Painted for the Florentine Badia, this Annunciation represents the peak of Lorenzo Monaco's work; in the period in which Masaccio, initiator of the artistic Renaissance, was beginning to work, the Medieval world is brought to life with brilliant success in this work (c. 1418).

12

RUSSIAN SCHOOL
St. Catherine

Catherine is portrayed with her usual attributes, i.e. the palm of martyrdom in her right hand and the hooked wheel on which she was tortured before her head was cut off. The image (18th century) is decorated with a crown and a fine silver-gilt frame.

International Gothic Room

The works

1. GHERARDO STARNINA
Virgin and Child with St. John the Baptist, St. Nicolas and Angels
c. 1407-1410
Tempera on wood; 103×58 cm
Inv. 1890 no. 441. Restored: 1990

2. MASTER OF BORGO ALLA COLLINA
Madonna with Child and Saints (Anthony Abbot, John the Baptist, Lawrence and Peter)
In the cuspid:
The Crucifix between St. Sebastian and St. Julian
c. 1420
Tempera on wood; 192×87,5 cm
Inv. 1890 no. 478. Restored: 2001

3. MASTER OF THE STRAUS MADONNA
Annunciation
1400-1410
Tempera on wood; 212×219 cm
Inv. 1890 no. 3146

4. MASTER OF THE STRAUS MADONNA
St. Catherine of Alexandria St. Francis
c. 1400-1410
Tempera on wood; 63×31 cm (each)
Inv. 1890 nos. 476, 477

5. FLORENTINE PAINTER
St. Peter and St. Eustace
(On the back: *The prophet Jeremiah and Angel's head*);
St. Nicolas and St. Peter
(On the back: *The Prophet Isaiah [?] and Angel's head*);
St. Reparata (or Dorothy) and St. James
(On the back: *Angel with thurible*);
St. Jerome and Saint with book
(On the back: *Angel with thurible*)
c. 1410
Tempera on wood; 64×26 cm (each)
Inv. 1890 nos. 6116, 6117, 6118, 6132
Restored: 1995

6. MASTER OF SANT'IVO (above)
Madonna with Child and Saints (Anthony Abbot, Francis of Assisi, Dorothea and a Saint)
c. 1400-1415
Tempera on wood; 77×42 cm
Inv. 1890 no. 8614

7. MASTER OF SANT'IVO (below)
Madonna and Child with four Saints (Apollonia, John the Baptist, Anthony Abbot and a Saint)
c. 1390-1410
Tempera on wood; 70×51,5 cm
Inv. 1890 no. 3151

8. GIOVANNI TOSCANI
Incredulity of St. Thomas; The Prophets Jeremiah and Isaiah (cuspide)
c. 1420
Tempera on wood; 242×123 cm
Inv. 1890 no. 457

9. GIOVANNI TOSCANI
Crucifixion (cuspids)
In the predella:
Stigmata of St. Francis and *Miracle of St. Nicolas of Bari*
c. 1423-1424
Tempera on wood; 125×46 and 45×72 cm
Inv. 1890 nos. 6089 et 3333
Restored: 1986

10. GIOVANNI TOSCANI
Madonna and Child with two musical Angels and two Saints
1423-1424
Tempera on wood; 148×102 cm
Inv. 1890 no. 5919. Restored: 1986

11. MASTER OF THE SHERMAN PREDELLA
Crucifixion
c. 1415-1430; Tempera on wood;
45×80 cm. Inv. 1890 no. 4654

12. MASTER OF BORGO ALLA COLLINA
Enthroned Madonna with Child and Saints
c. 1430
Tempera on wood; 140×67 cm
Inv. 1890 no. 3159

13. ROSSELLO DI JACOPO FRANCHI
Madonna and Child with Saints (John the Baptist and Francis, Mary Magdalene and Matthew)
In the cuspids:
Crucifixion with Saints
First half of XV century
Tempera on wood; 238×198 cm
Inv. 1890 no. 475

14. BICCI DI LORENZO
Mystic marriage of St. Catherine
c. 1423-1425
Tempera on wood; 127×62 cm
Inv. 1890 no. 8611

15. BICCI DI LORENZO
St. Lawrence
In the predella: *Scenes from the Life of St. Lawrence*
c. 1428
Tempera on wood; 236×99 cm
Inv. 1890 no. 471

16. MASTER OF 1416
Virgin with Child and Saints (Anthony Abbot and Peter, Julian and John the Baptist)
In the cuspid: *Ethernal Father*
1416
Tempera on wood; 231×122 cm
Inv. 1890 no. 4635

17. MASTER OF THE STRAUS MADONNA
Triptych: Madonna and Child between St. Matthew and the Archangel Michael
c. 1385
Tempera on wood
141×196 cm
Inv. 1890 no. 3072

18. MASTER OF THE STRAUS MADONNA
Christ as the Man of Sorrows with the symbols of Passion
c. 1400-1405
Tempera on wood
123×240 cm
Inv. dep. no. 14
Restored: 1983

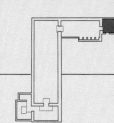

1

GHERARDO STARNINA
Madonna with Child,
St. John the Baptist, St. Nicolas and Angels

Gherardo Starnina, a Florentine painter who also worked in Spain where he came into contact with the most advanced trends of International Gothicism, today tends to be identified by critics as the so-called Master of the Lively Child, an outstanding figure in early Fifteenth century painting in Florence. He was noted for his linear finesse and the decorative nature of his elegant forms, and is almost a profane *alter ego* of Lorenzo Monaco.

3

MASTER
OF THE STRAUS MADONNA
Annunciation

This work came from the leper Hospital of Sant'Eusebio al Prato and is attributed to a painter who was active between the end of the Fourteenth century and the beginning of the Fifteenth. His identity is not known and he is usually known as the Master of the Straus Madonna from a *Virgin with Child* in the Straus Collection. This is a painter gifted with fine sensitivity to colour and who also pays attention to the volumetric structure of bodies and the perspective depth of the space.

9

GIOVANNI TOSCANI
Stigmata of St. Francis
and *Miracle of St. Nicolas of Bari* (predella)

These two panels, dating from the beginning of the third decade of the Fifteenth century, formed part of the polyptych adorning the Ardinghelli Chapel in the Church of Santa Trinita at Florence. The painter was a Florentine artist, enrolled in the Compagnia di San Luca in 1424, known especially as a painter of chests (two of his chests are now in the Bargello Museum). His earliest works, such the *Incredulity of St. Thomas* in the Accademia Gallery, reveal training in contact with the Orcagna circle as well as the influence of Lorenzo Ghiberti's style, particularly in the rhythmic folds of the drapery.

This element has led some scholars to identify the artist as Giovanni di Francesco, one of Ghiberti's assistants for the doors of the Baptistery. Within a span of ten years Giovanni Toscani shows in these two panels how he has assimilated the innovations of the International Gothic Style introduced to Florence by Gentile da Fabriano and Arcangelo di Cola.

BICCI DI LORENZO
St. Lawrence

This panel comes from the Laical Company devoted to St. Peter at the Church of San Pietro a Monticelli. The Saint is shown standing on the symbol of his martyrdom, the grille, while in his left hand he holds the palm and in the right a red banner with a gold star, perhaps the insignia of the Company who commissioned the work. In the predella, in the right-hand scene, St. Lawrence is depicted freeing souls from Purgatory, according to the legend which claims that as he died on Good Friday, he was permitted every Friday to repeat Christ's descent to the Underworld. The scene on the left shows the martyrdom inflicted on him by his persecutors. Bicci di Lorenzo painted this work in about 1428, in collaboration with Stefano d'Antonio with whom he 'kept company' (or as we would say today 'was in partnership') from 1426 to 1434.

Index